EVESHAM

Please return/renew this item by the last date shown

 **worcestershire**
countycouncil
Cultural Services

WOLFREN RIVERSTICK

70003016854X

First Edition

A CIP catalogue recording for this book is available from the British Library

ISBN 0-9554314-0-9
ISBN 97809554314-0-1

Cover illustration by Michelle Martin of Willowmoor Art Workshop, 76 Crackley Bank, Chesterton, Newcastle-under-Lyme

Book design by Antony Rowe Ltd

Typeset by Crazy Wolf Books
Published by Crazy Wolf Books

Printed and bound in England by Antony Rowe Ltd, Bumper's Farm, Chippenham, Wilts, SN14 6LH

For Dusty,

the wildest, craziest, most wonderful cat that ever existed

A CAT'S LOG OF EVENTS

CHAPTER ONE

The Mighty White Oak Tree

"Where are you going?" asked the young girl.

"Mind your own business," replied her brother.

"What have you got in that rucksack?" said the girl as she moved towards him and tried to take a peek inside the bag.

The boy quickly pushed his sister away.

"Just go home will ya," he snapped.

"No, not until you tell me where you're going."

"If you don't beat it I'll kick your butt from here to Kingdom Come."

But the girl didn't beat it and, without warning, she tried to snatch the rucksack from her brother which fell onto the dry, dusty ground with a thud. She immediately leapt upon it, fumbling about in excited anticipation as she tried to untie the drawstrings that held it together. In retaliation the boy pounced upon his sister, grabbed her long hair and yanked her aside in a rough manner.

"Ouch! That hurts," she cried in pain.

"It's meant to! I thought I told you to clear off. Now do as you're told... GO HOME."

"Yeow, ow, ouch... Let go of my hair!" the girl continued to squeal.

"Only if you promise to go away and leave me alone."

"Okay, I promise."

The girl quickly broke her promise however, because at the very moment the boy released the tight grip he had on his sister's hair she sprang forward and snatched at the rucksack once more. This time she was more successful in her attempt to seize the bag when one of the straps gave way, giving her the opportunity to pull it away from her brother. A vicious struggle then took place as the boy attempted to regain possession of his rucksack and, although she was wrestling hard against her younger brother's superior strength, somehow or other the girl eventually managed to untie the drawstring that held the rucksack shut and this exposed part of the contents when they spilled out onto the ground.

At this point the boy lashed out angrily, striking his sister on the side of the head and knocking her down. Knowing that she had been defeated the stunned girl decided to remain where she had fallen onto the hard, dried-up muddy track beside the river, propping herself up with one arm and rubbing the sore abrasion on her head with her free hand, while she watched her brother stuff his belongings back into the rucksack and retie the drawstring.

"Why are you carrying a hammer and copper pins in your bag?" asked the girl. "...And that's a length of rope you've got there, isn't it?"

"Mind your own business Ellie," snarled the boy as he retied the drawstring on the rucksack.

"Oh, I get it... Now I know what you're up to. You're going to try and climb the old oak tree aren't you?" she said knowingly.

The boy said nothing. He picked up his precious rucksack, flung it over his left shoulder and began to walk away.

"You know you're not supposed to climb trees – especially that one! I'm going to tell Mum and then you'll be for it," Ellie shouted after him.

Upon hearing this remark her brother stopped dead in his tracks and turned around before replying with a threat of his own.

"You snitch! If you tell Mum what I'm doing, then I'll tell her that you've been hanging out with Maddie Jones and her gang because you know you're not allowed to do that either. And I'll tell her you've been helping yourself to money out of her purse too... So there!"

"Hey, it was you that took her money, not me; I don't do things like that," she retorted rather indignantly.

"Yeah, but Mum doesn't know that. She's more likely to believe me, isn't she? As far as she's concerned I can't do a thing wrong in her eyes... Thinks the sun shines out of my butt, she does."

"Don't I know it," sneered the boy's sister. "You're always sucking up to her."

"So what if I am? It pays off when it matters most, don't it?"

"Creep!"

"I ain't no creep; I'm just her blue-eyed boy because I'm the youngest, and I always will be."

"You might always be the youngest, but I'll always be the cutest", boasted Ellie in an attempt to break even with the verbal battle she was already beginning to lose.

"Call yourself cute? Have you looked in the mirror lately, Spotty?"

"I can't help it," said Ellie with tears in her eyes, and the only defence she could find to that remark was to stick her tongue out at her brother.

"Spotty!" repeated the boy, and then he followed it up by chanting the words "pizza face!"

"Leave me alone," shouted Ellie as she burst into floods of tears.

The boy grinned smugly when his sister began to cry knowing that he'd got the upper hand again.

"You know what Dad always tells us," cried the girl in one last effort to prevent her brother from paying a visit to the oak tree.

"Who cares what Dad tells us?"

"I do," sobbed Ellie. "Anyway, Dad says that curiosity killed the cat."

"Huh! Who cares about cats either? Be seein' ya Spotty Old Pizza Face," he taunted cruelly before finally walking away.

When the boy arrived at the foot of Sunrise Hill he found that it was shrouded in mist like it so often was and he couldn't even see more than halfway up the hill let alone the peak. But within moments of his arrival the mist mysteriously cleared away to reveal the mighty white oak tree perched on top of the grassy slopes where it had proudly been for maybe 300 years or more, its gnarled, twisted limbs stretching eerily into the air like ghostly white fingers beckoning him towards it.

For a while he stood admiring the quiet giant above him, the distinctive silhouette of its spooky-looking shape dominating the skyline. Ever since he could remember the boy had always wanted to climb this tree and had vowed that one day he would do exactly that, but now the time had come to take on this challenge the boy felt nervous as he thought about the stories which circulated regarding this particular oak tree.

Legend had it that the tree was haunted, perhaps possessed by evil spirits, although nobody knew for sure. Folklore told that it was once a noble warrior who, when he passed into the next world, became immortalised in wood to preserve the man's heart and soul forever. Apparently, the hard texture of the tree's knotty grain was the warrior's strength that would forever remain with him, while the thick, coarse bark was his tough skin and the outstretched limbs were the warrior's arms, welcoming anyone or anything that came within his reach but never letting go again. The boy shuddered at this thought and he tried not to feel afraid. His friends were afraid though, but they were nothing but cissies as far as he was concerned so he had to climb the tree just to show them he wasn't a cissy like them.

After psyching himself up ready for his conquest the boy eventually trekked uphill to where the tree towered over him like a pale, mystical giant and appeared even more menacing now that he was right up close. It was very blustery on top of Sunrise Hill and any leaves that had been on the tree's branches now lay silently on

11

the hilltop or swirled manically around in the late autumn air. One particularly large oak tree leaf flew around his head several times before slapping the boy in the face, making his cheeks smart and almost forcing him to jump out of his skin.

If that wasn't enough to frighten him, the wind made the most uncanny wailing sound when it blew between the tree's bare branches overhead, causing a shiver to run down the boy's spine again as he stopped to listen. He was sure that he could occasionally hear faint meowing sounds coming from the tree as if there were cats trapped inside it, but he shrugged this off as a ludicrous idea and the sound was simply the distant bleating of sheep in the fields surrounding Sunrise Hill, their far-away cries carried high into the air on the strong afternoon breeze.

However, little did he realize that the great white oak was a very special tree indeed and it harboured a deep, dark secret because it was actually the Earthgate to a nether world known as Catland! You see, deep within the bowels of Sunrise Hill, far beneath its innocent-looking grass-covered surface, there lay a labyrinth of tunnels which led to an underground kingdom where cats were its dwellers. Here was a place where all the cats in the country congregated; whether they were trying to escape their owners for a while or whether they were lost or homeless, this was a land where they could chill out until they were ready to move on again.

(So, if you have ever wondered why your cherished pet cat sometimes disappears for several hours – or even several days – then now you know the reason why.)

Completely unaware of this secret world beneath his feet the boy placed his rucksack against the bole of the tree, untied the drawstring and removed the length of rope which he draped around the immense tree trunk. Then he wrapped the rope around his own body too and looped the ends into a slipknot that would pull taut when the pressure of his weight was applied against it but it would not come undone. (His dad had taught him to do this because he was once employed as a truck driver and he had to tie knots like these to secure the vehicle's load.)

Having satisfied himself that the rope would hold his weight when he leant back against it the boy began to climb the tree. To begin with there were a few foot and handholds carved by nature into the lower section of the oak tree's massive beam as if someone had chiselled them deliberately for the purpose of climbing. How they had got to be there nobody seemed to know but they existed nonetheless and this helped to make the first climbing stage an easy hurdle to overcome. Like a monkey, the boy clambered nimbly upwards making use of these natural grips but afterwards the going became considerably tougher. This did not deter the boy though because he had prepared himself for his mission.

Keeping his toes planted firmly in the footholds, he leaned backwards, placed his weight against the rope and began to hammer a long copper pin into the tree's heartwood which would give him an extra climbing support. Immediately there was a strange high-pitched squealing sound and a blood-red sticky sap oozed from the bark of the tree which trickled all over his hands. The boy looked at the gooey sap in disgust.

"Ooh, gross!" he muttered out loud.

And then he tried to wipe his hands clean on the rough surface of the tree trunk but the sap stuck to his skin like glue, seeming to become stickier than ever. No matter how hard he tried the boy couldn't remove the tacky sap, and eventually he gave up trying to get rid of it and returned to the job in hand. After hammering home a second copper pin, once again the awful red sap spilled from the hole... and there was that weird squeal again. The boy stared at his hands for a second time. It really was some disgusting stuff that came out of the tree which made his hands appear as if they were covered in blood, but the show must go on and this wasn't going to put him off climbing to the top of the magnificent oak tree.

It was a slow process but steadily the boy began to make progress. At this particular point of the climb he was feeling exceptionally pleased with himself because, to his knowledge, nobody had ever scaled the oak tree to such a great height. Now there was only a short distance to go before he would be at the halfway mark where the tree's branches began to thicken and spread. He had heard stories that in the past anyone who had reached the lower branches of the tree had never returned to the ground again; apparently, they had disappeared forever and were never to be seen again as if they had simply vanished into thin air. Of course, he disbelieved these ridiculous stories and put them down to simply being make-believe old wives' tales.

At last the boy reached the lowest branches, some fifteen feet from the ground, and he heaved himself up. Here he sat upon a huge branch taking a much-needed breather whilst contemplating the next leg of his epic climb, the leg that would take him to the crook of the tree where several boughs fanned out in all directions. From there on it would be plain sailing to the uppermost reaches he thought, although there was still a lot of work to do just to get to the crook.

When he eventually arrived at the wide crook of the tree the boy stood upright amidst the tangle of gigantic boughs that surrounded him, looking down upon the ground that was now far below. Although he was greatly chuffed at his achievement he was wondering how he would get down from the tree; this was going to be another feat altogether and maybe this was why stories had been bandied about that no-one returned to the ground because they simply couldn't get down. A thought began to trouble the boy's mind and he warily glanced around him, searching the area to check that there were no skeletons of previous climbers lingering amongst the tree's branches. Then he laughed at this ludicrous idea and got on with the task of continuing upwards.

At the very moment when he stretched out his arms to grab an overhead branch in order to pull himself up a loud commotion broke out above his head. Suddenly, several squirrels appeared out of nowhere. There were dozens of them, and they were red in colour. The boy was greatly alarmed by the presence of these daintily-featured creatures with their finely tufted ears and bushy tails, and his surprise was doubled because he had never before seen red squirrels. They were, in fact, quite a rare species that had chosen this sturdy oak tree as their safe haven after driving out their arch enemies the grey squirrel from its lofty branches. The occupants of Catland didn't like grey squirrels because they were basically vermin who were destroying their beloved tree by eating its exterior, so they were extremely grateful to the red squirrel clan for getting rid of the pesky varmints. In return for ridding the great oak of its intruders the Ruler of Catland appointed Sciurus, Queen of the Reds, as guardian of this very tree whereupon her clan became the protectors of the great white oak.

"Get away from me, you awful creatures," yelled the boy, waving his arms about angrily in the hope that the squirrels would run away.

However, this seemed to make the tree's protectors noisier than ever and the squirrels continued to chatter away, hissing and spitting at him with all their rage.

"What is it with you? Get lost!" he demanded.

But instead of disappearing, the army of squirrels advanced upon him. The boy hurriedly retreated, cowering down in terror whilst flailing his arms around like a demented thing, until he stumbled backwards and lost his balance. Then he fell, and at that precise instant the centre of the tree trunk appeared to open up like the jaws of a huge beast and swallow him whole.

He plummeted like a stone, falling down deeper and deeper into the endless hollow of the tree, not once touching the sides, until he ceased to fall any further. Fortunately, a split-second before he was about to make contact with the ground as if it was through some sort of natural instinct, he twisted his body and landed on his feet. Then there was a flash of brilliant light, just like a lightning strike, followed by temporary darkness.

CHAPTER TWO

In the Court of The Catmaster

When the pitch black darkness turned back into a state of light again the boy began to feel strange – somehow different and not his usual self at all. He couldn't put his finger on whatever it was that made him feel so odd, that is until he began to lick his right paw.

PAW? He didn't have paws!

He glanced down at the ground and to his utmost amazement now he did... Not one paw (that would be ridiculous anyway), not two, nor three; no, he had four paws. Closing his eyes, he slowly counted to ten. Then he opened them again. Sure enough, there were definitely four paws – one on each corner. Suddenly, and incredibly, he had grown two extra legs with a paw on the end of each one. In other words he had turned into a quadruped.

('Quadruped' was a word he had recently found in a dictionary purely by chance – oh, how he hated dictionaries because they were so difficult to use and the words were never where they were supposed to be. He wasn't even looking for this particular word but it had jumped out of the page at him and for some unknown reason he felt compelled to understand what it meant. After learning that a quadruped was basically a four-footed creature he had closed the dictionary and never did find the word he was really searching for.)

So, now that he knew what he had suddenly become, what variety of quadruped was he? He turned his head to look at his body, and then at his tail.

TAIL?

Now he had a bushy, scruffy-looking tail as well… and strangely-patterned mottled fur too, multi-coloured predominantly in shades of orange, brown, black and white. At this point he realized that he had inexplicably turned into a cat, and a tortoiseshell cat at that. All of a sudden he had become an ordinary-looking, short-haired moggy and, oh, how he hated cats, especially the tortoishell variety! (In fact, he despised them almost as much as he hated dictionaries.) Of all the creatures in the World why did he have to transform into a cat, he puzzled? Then he began to wonder how this could possibly have happened to him. Perhaps he had bumped his head when he fell, or maybe he was just dreaming the whole thing. There was no logical explanation for it whatsoever, so surely this whole episode had to be a figment of his imagination.

The next question that sprang into his muddled mind was: where on Earth was he? And 'earth' really was the key word because it was obvious that he was underground for the walls, floor and ceiling were made of dried mud, with tree roots poking through here and there. In that case he reckoned that he must be beneath the great white oak, but how could this be? There was no trace above him of the hollow tree whose deep inners he had supposedly fallen down; and somehow or other he had finished up in a tunnel that dead-ended where he now stood. This made it a cul-de-sac in effect with no visible means of an exit to the outside world, therefore he couldn't have got there any other way than through the hollow centre of the oak tree. The whole thing was very mysterious.

With no place else to go, he set off along the earthen tunnel in the only direction that he could. Where he was going to he had no clue, but, oddly enough, there were signposts every so often with the words 'THIS WAY' written on them as if he was meant to follow them... So he did.

Shortly, he rounded a curve in the tunnel where two huge, red tabby cats suddenly loomed before him. The pair of ginger tomcats were sitting upright, facing each other like book ends on either side of an arched wooden doorway, giving him the impression that they were guarding it. Oddly, one of them (the more muscular of the two) wore an eye patch over his left eye whilst the other had a red bandana with white polka dots all over it that was slung loosely around his thick neck. These two cats really did look quite strange and he found it very difficult to take his eyes off them. The ginger toms also eyed the tortoiseshell with a similar curiosity as he approached them and when he was right up close the one with the eye patch spoke to him in a gruff voice.

"Oh, there you are," he said. "You took your time getting here, didn't you? Come along now, look lively, they're waiting for you."

"Who is waiting for me?" asked the tortoiseshell, but he got no reply.

Meanwhile, the second ginger sentry silently opened the wooden door and ushered the perplexed tortoiseshell through it. Then both of the guards followed him inside, shutting the door firmly behind them.

The room behind the door was a large chamber where rows of stone benches that looked similar to church pews filled the interior, arranged in a crescent shape around a stone pulpit. Sat upon these stone benches were cats – lots of them that came in many different breeds – who stared at him as he was roughly pushed along a narrow aisle in their midst with the ginger toms hot on his heels. Never before had the tortoiseshell seen so many cats together in one place.

"Stand here", demanded the same sentry who had earlier spoken to him when he finally reached the stone pulpit.

At a loss for words the tortoiseshell did exactly as he was told and halted on the spot awaiting further instructions from his odd guards. There followed a brief interlude whereupon the newly-formed cat took in his surroundings. In front of him was a long table, also made of stone, with a tall, beautifully carved throne behind it, while all around the room there were statues of sphinx cats similar to ones he had seen in pictures of ancient Egypt. It really was a curious place to be.

Meanwhile, the strange gathering of cats remained silent, their keen eyes glued to both the throne and their new visitor, whilst they patiently waited for something to happen. After a short time had elapsed one of the cats that was seated at one end of the table jumped up in the air as if an electric current had passed through his chair at that very moment.

"ALL RISE!" he commanded, shrieking enthusiastically.

This suddenly animated cat was a skinny fellow and quite weird-looking too with his wide, boggling eyes and over-size ears that seemed too big for his tiny peanut-shaped, pixie-like head – the tortoiseshell had never seen a cat of the breed known as Devon Rex before.

Upon this zanily-acting creature's command the occupants of the courtroom immediately got to their feet as a door behind the stone table opened into the room and a majestic figure entered the chamber dressed in red robes the shade of crimson and a pointed hat that matched, his entire outfit decorated with moons and stars. If this cat was a wizard then it was the nearest thing to one that the tortoiseshell had ever seen. A pair of half-spectacles, also moon-shaped, hung on a chain around the cat's neck, and a mass of thick fur, blue-grey in colour, billowed out from wherever it could. The wizard-type cat sat down upon the solitary throne and nodded his head at his skinny assistant.

"Thank-you Gubbins," said the wizardly cat in an authoritarian yet kindly voice.

"Please be seated," Gubbins said in a much more sedate tone than before as he addressed his audience.

All of the cats sat down, except for one.

"I don't have a seat," complained the tortoiseshell.

"Silence in court", demanded the ginger sentry with the gruff voice. At the same time he cuffed the tortoiseshell around his left ear.

"Ouch, that hurt!" the tortoiseshell groaned in pain.

"It was meant to… Do those words sound at all familiar to you?" growled the ginger tom.

21

"That's enough, Trojan," the blue-furred wizard intervened.

"Sorry M'lord," Trojan apologized.

In that instant the tortoiseshell cat realized that the ginger sentry was referring to the very same words he had said to his sister when he had aggressively tugged at her hair.

"Is that why I'm in court – just for hitting my sister and pulling her hair?" he asked, still rubbing his left ear because it was now smarting.

"That, and other reasons too," replied the wizard cat. "Allow me to introduce myself: my name is Harlequin, The Catmaster. Welcome to the kingdom of Catland where I am Supreme Grandmaster. I am a feline (that's means 'cat' to you) of the breed known as Russian Blue…"

"I thought I could detect a slight foreign accent," the tortoiseshell interrupted.

"…BE QUIET! You will speak only when spoken to and you will also do as you are told. As you have already experienced, we are not afraid to issue punishment here in Catland – unlike your mortal world where people seem to get away with anything nowadays!"

The tortoiseshell took no notice at all of what Harlequin was saying and he defiantly interrupted again.

"What have you done to me? Why am I now a cat? I demand to know."

"Whatever has been done to you, has been brought about by yourself through your own misgivings," Harlequin patiently informed him. "We are here merely to teach you a lesson that you will never forget."

Then Harlequin briefly turned his attention elsewhere.

"Could I have the offence sheet please Scarlet."

Upon Harlequin's request a red squirrel instantly bounded across the flagstone floor and handed a thick wad of paperwork to The Catmaster.

"Thank-you," he said.

Slightly abashed, young Scarlet the courtroom junior smiled sweetly at Harlequin before scampering back to her desk. Meanwhile, Harlequin raised his spectacles towards his face and put them on. Then he began to browse through the numerous sheets of paper that he now held in his paws, occasionally shaking his head disapprovingly. Finally he placed the paperwork onto the polished stone surface of the table in front of him, clasped his paws together and spoke again.

"Tut-tut! You have been a naughty boy, haven't you? You appear to be a thoroughly bad piece of work by all accounts, and an out-of-control tearaway. What do you have to say for yourself?"

The tortoiseshell glanced at the skinny cat called Gubbins, as if to seek permission to speak.

"You may answer The Catmaster," said Gubbins.

"I... I don't know what you mean?" said the tortoiseshell in astonishment. "I haven't done anything wrong as far as I'm concerned."

"Hmm!" said Harlequin in a doubtful voice. "In that case let me just read out some of the offences to you.

"Number One: BULLYING your sister on a regular basis."

"She usually starts it," retorted the tortoiseshell.

"She is purely defending herself young fellow, as anyone would do in such a situation."

"Yeah? Well, so what! She deserves what she gets anyway."

"It is obvious that the boy has no regrets; mark this next one down in the book please Magenta..." said The Catmaster turning towards one of the squirrels who was seated at the opposite end of the table to Gubbins. Magenta was the court recorder who was quickly scribbling down notes in squirrel-squeak shorthand which would be translated into cat lingo later.

"...Offence Number Two:" Harlequin continued, "LACK OF REMORSE!

"Three: STEALING from your mother. Not a very good trait at all is that one – we call this biting off the hand that feeds you. Your mother is temporarily a single parent I believe... How despicable of you! She's struggling to raise you and your sister on her own, with not much household income; she goes without so you can have whatever you want, and she works long hours to provide dinner on the table and a roof over her children's heads. And how do you repay her? BY STEALING! Where is your father by the way?"

"He's no longer with us," the tortoiseshell sneered.

"Then where is he?"

"He's... he's dead!"

"No, I don't believe he is," Harlequin replied. "In fact, I know he isn't dead... What an awful lie to tell about your own father."

The tortoiseshell quickly changed his tune to try and cover up his terrible lie.

"Okay, so he's not dead really; I was just joking... He's gone on

24

holiday if you must know."

"Tut, tut! That's not strictly the truth either, is it? In actual fact your father has had to leave home hasn't he?"

If a tortoiseshell cat's face could redden with the embarrassment of being found out, then that's exactly what it did.

"Y-y-yes," stammered the tortoiseshell. "But how do you know that?"

"We know everything about you", replied the Catmaster. "Put that one in your book too Magenta...

"Number Four: LIAR!

"Let me tell the jury the reason why your father has had to leave home; or do you want to tell them yourself?"

The tortoiseshell cat hung his head in embarrassment but said nothing.

"No, I didn't think you would want to tell everyone. Very well, then I shall explain... The poor man couldn't cope with his son's bad behaviour any longer folks – always in trouble of some sort and always blaming someone else. Not only that, but he was causing a rift between his mother and father because the boy's mum did not want to admit that her son was a thoroughly bad lot. The only way out that his father could see was to run away because he thought that he was the bad influence on his son. *HE* was the one that really drove his father away," concluded Harlequin, raising his voice and pointing a long, sharp claw in the direction of the accused tortoiseshell.

"I... I don't have to take this from a cat," the tortoiseshell said in a shaky voice. "Either this is some kind of joke, or I must be dreaming."

"A joke? DO YOU SEE ME LAUGHING?" roared Harlequin. "…And, no, you are definitely not dreaming – this is very real indeed."

For the first time in his life the tortoiseshell began to feel frightened, but Harlequin was relentless with his barrage of accusations as he went on reading from his list.

"Five: CRUELTY to animals. For instance: pulling wings and legs off insects; setting fire to snail shells so you can watch them explode; cracking the glass on fish tanks so that the water seeps out; shooting birds with an air pistol; kicking small animals, especially cats (tortoiseshell ones mainly!) And so it goes on… Don't you like animals?"

"I'm not fussed about them really," the tortoiseshell replied shrugging his shoulders at the same time.

"And now you're a cat, the one creature you despise more than any other," taunted Harlequin.

The tortoiseshell shrugged his shoulders again as if he didn't care.

"Why don't you like cats, tortoiseshell ones in particular?" asked Harlequin.

"They're ugly and I don't like the colour of their fur."

"How ironic it is that you should end up as a tortoiseshell then, isn't it?" said Harlequin with a wry grin on his face. He shook his head despairingly and continued to reel off the list of offences.

"Number Six: LACK OF RESPECT – that is, for anyone or anything. Take our oak tree for example."

"Eh?" uttered the tortoiseshell with a puzzled expression on his face. "What are you talking about? I like that tree, I've always wanted to climb it."

"Yes, but for the wrong reasons. The only reason you wanted to climb the tree was to be better than everyone else, and so that you could boast about it to your so-called friends. They're not your friends really you know – they're afraid of you because you bully them. As for our tree: you drove metal spikes into its body and made it bleed... We could hear its cries from here. Now you have its blood on your hands."

The tortoiseshell looked at his front paws in horror which were still covered with sticky red stains of tree sap. Then he hurriedly rubbed his paws together as he tried to get rid of the sap but it was to no avail because the stains were there to stay.

"However," Harlequin continued, "given time the oak tree will heal with a little help from its friends, for we in Catland are its friends as well as its keepers. Had it been a less substantial species than a *quercus* – that's the Latin word for oak by the way – it would have dwindled away after being stabbed through the heart by a copper nail, you know."

"So, what's the problem then?" the tortoiseshell wilfully remarked.

"And, still no remorse..." said Harlequin shaking his head in disappointment.

"...Number Seven: Being in possession of A BAD ATTITUDE!

"Eight: SELFISHNESS – It appears that you only care about yourself. You seem to take great delight in going out of your way to get what you want and it doesn't matter who you hurt along the way.

"And lastly – but by no means least – Number Nine (although this

27

crime actually comes at the top of our list): the dreadful act of CATSLAUGHTER!"

There was a sharp intake of breath from the jury upon hearing this word.

"*Catslaughter?* What the heck does that mean?" asked the tortoiseshell.

"MURDER!" Harlequin emphasized.

"*MURDER?*" gasped the tortoisehell. "What on Earth are you talking about now?"

"Only last week you killed one of our family; a poor, defenceless cat."

There was another sharp intake of breath amongst the gathering followed by muffled whispering. Meanwhile, the tortoiseshell was scratching his head in bewilderment as he tried to rack his brains.

"Don't you remember? Let me jog your memory... You were on your skateboard when the incident happened... after you jumped over a wall and landed on a park bench," Harlequin reminded him.

"Oh that cat!" retorted the young tortoiseshell nonchalantly as he recalled the event. "Anyway, I didn't kill it – I just winged it."

"She passed away later from her injuries. You didn't even attempt to help her at the time of the incident and you therefore left her to perish alone."

"It was an accident," wailed the tortoiseshell. His head was spinning around in complete shock by now. "How was I supposed to know that a cat was sleeping on the other side of the wall? I didn't do it on purpose you know."

"Hmm... Whether it was deliberate or not, the matter will be taken into account when the jury make up their mind what to do with you. In the meantime, you will be escorted to the Limbo Room by Trojan and Spartan where you will await your punishment," Harlequin concluded in a stern voice.

The stunned tortoiseshell cat was thus led away by the two ginger sentries and taken to an adjoining room. There was no furniture in this room where another cat sat alone on the cold, bare flagstone floor. Together, the two cats remained in silence for some time until, eventually, the second cat spoke to him.

"My name's Phillip," he announced.

"So what?"

"I was just trying to make polite conversation. I could be your friend if you want – you look as if you need a friend right now."

"I don't need a friend."

"Suit yourself."

There was another long silence.

"Phillip? That's a weird name for a cat," said the tortoiseshell at length.

"It's not a weird name at all! In fact, I think it's perfectly normal if you ask me," retorted Phillip who felt slightly offended at the suggestion his name was weird.

"I didn't really mean your name was weird – I meant to say it was a plain name for a cat."

"Well, why don't you say what you mean instead of unnecessarily upsetting everyone?"

The tortoiseshell just stared at Phillip in disbelief.

"It's not too late to apologize you know," said Phillip holding his nose in the air.

"There is nothing to apologize for," replied the tortoiseshell arrogantly.

"Please yourself… Anyway, it doesn't matter now whether you apologize or not."

Another silence followed but the tortoiseshell soon became bored.

"So how come you've got such a plain name as Phillip?" he asked.

"I thought you'd never ask… Harlequin chose my name for me, but I've always been called Phillip anyway."

"My Dad's name is Phillip too," said the tortoiseshell and then he sighed loudly when he thought about his parents and how much he was already missing them.

"Jolly good," replied Phillip quickly glossing over the subject. "What are you called by the way?"

"I can't remember my name," said the tortoiseshell. "Now that really is weird! I guess I must have bumped my head when I fell through the tree and now I've lost my memory or something."

"Don't worry; your name will come back to you one way or another," Phillip reassured the young tortoiseshell.

"Do you think so?"

"Oh, I know so!"

"Are you waiting here to be punished too?" asked the tortoiseshell.

"Oh no; in the past I've already been punished enough. Actually I'm waiting here to be given a new identity by The Catmaster. I shall be reborn soon, possibly under a different name – who knows. I've got a whole new life to look forward to now, so I don't really care what my name is."

"So, you didn't do anything wrong then?" said the tortoiseshell in surprise.

"No, I'm simply a wandering cat; a gypsy if you like... I've made a few mistakes in the past but I've never done anything wrong. When you can hold up your hands – or paws for that matter – and admit you've made mistakes or done wrong then you know that everything is going to be alright and you won't go down the wrong path again."

"I wish I could say the same."

"Yes, it sounds as if you're in a spot of bother from what I hear. They're probably going to throw the book at you."

"What book?"

"It's a figure of speech," laughed Phillip, nudging his new companion in a friendly manner. "It roughly means that you've done so many things wrong you'll probably be given every sentence that's in the rule book – not literally though. In other words, you're in big trouble."

Phillip laughed again.

"It's not funny!" snapped the tortoiseshell.

"Oh, but it is. You've got to laugh... What else can you do? I mean, you're going to have to pay for what you've done so you'll just have to grin and bear it. And you can't go through life putting the blame on everyone either because eventually the time will always come when you have to suffer the consequences of your crimes. It's your own fault that you're here and nobody else's."

31

At that point of the conversation the door creaked open and the bulky shapes of the two ginger tomcats filled its framework.

"Come along Phillip, it's your turn to see The Catmaster now," said Trojan.

"Okay Trojan, I'm coming," said Phillip. Then he turned to speak to his new friend, the tortoiseshell cat.

"Keep your nose clean, do what you're supposed to do, and you'll be out of here in no time at all. See you on the outside Son... And don't forget to keep smiling."

With that, Phillip departed with the two sentries leaving the tortoiseshell cat all alone again, wrapped up in his lonely thoughts. The future looked bleak for him and he felt thoroughly miserable.

CHAPTER THREE

The Sentence of Nine Lives

The tortoiseshell cat was not left alone for long. A short while after Phillip had left the room, Trojan and Spartan returned to collect the confused animal and they marched him straight back to the courtroom.

"Please be seated," ordered Gubbins.

Everyone sat down, including the tortoiseshell.

"Except for you!" snapped Trojan as he stamped hard on the tortoiseshell's tail.

Letting out an evil screeching and hissing sound the tortoiseshell cat leapt high into the air, at the same time turning upon his antagonist and lashing out with outstretched claws but Trojan easily managed to dodge the clumsy swipes at his body.

"You'll have to learn to be quicker than that Kid if you want to survive in our world," sneered the sentry.

"I'll get even with you one of these days," promised the angry tortoiseshell.

Trojan laughed at this remark although he realized that the young animal would become quicker when he got used to being a cat and he may well get even with him one day.

"ORDER IN COURT," Gubbins screamed in his high-pitched, almost frenzied, voice. "We will not allow such an outburst."

"He stamped on my tail," wailed the tortoiseshell.

"Did you Trojan?" The Catmaster asked him.

"Sorry M'Lord, it was an accident."

"I doubt that very much," Harlequin sternly replied. "See me in my chambers after the trial. Discipline is one thing, but I will not tolerate bullying of any sort."

"Yes M'Lord," Trojan meekly replied, at the same time glowering at the tortoiseshell.

"Serves you right," said the tortoiseshell sneeringly.

"Silence!" demanded Gubbins. "Turn around and face The Catmaster; he will have the last word, not you."

The tortoiseshell reluctantly turned to face Harlequin, who took over the proceedings from that point.

"The jury has reached a decision and will now pass sentence upon the accused," The Catmaster told the packed courtroom. Then he reached beneath his table and pulled out a strange-looking object which he held in the air for all to see.

"You are to be given the Sentence of Nine Lives," said The Catmaster addressing the tortoiseshell. "This is a cat o'nine tails, a device invented by mankind with the intention of administering

34

punishment in a horrible manner. In olden times the guilty party would be subjected to at least forty lashes of this implement, which is basically a whip."

The tortoiseshell's face fell in dismay.

"So, you're going to beat me with that thing are you?" he asked.

"*Certainly not!*" replied Harlequin, appalled that the tortoiseshell could think such a thing. "We do not agree with such barbaric methods."

"Then what are you going to do with it?"

"If you will stop interrupting me, then I can explain," said The Catmaster in a patient voice.

The tortoiseshell immediately fell silent.

"Thank-you... Now, these nine tails hanging from this short staff are not really cats' tails at all; they are in fact strips of leather with each one signifying a life. In other words, nine lives have now been bestowed upon you in order for you to prove yourself of worth... one for every serious offence you have committed. It works thus: if you carry out nine good deeds – which isn't really too much to ask – you will thenceforth forget that any of this has ever happened, and you will be just as you were before, except a much better person for your experience. Are you following me?"

The tortoiseshell nodded his head.

"What if I don't carry out the nine good deeds?" he enquired.

"I'm glad you asked me that question because it shows that you are listening to me at least... Each time you do a bad deed you will lose a life (or more than one, depending on how bad the offence is). On the other hand, if you do a good deed you will be rewarded by having a life restored to you. There will be a certain time period in which to achieve various tasks or tests, at the end of which you may be returned to your mortal world if you survive with your lives intact."

"If I don't have any lives left at the end of the time period, what will happen to me then?" asked the tortoiseshell.

"If you run out of lives then you will remain in feline form for the remainder of your days," replied Harlequin. "You will *NEVER* be allowed to revert back to a mortal and your family and so-called friends will forget all about you. They will *NOT* even remember that you had ever existed because your life will be erased from their memories forever."

When he had finished this sentence Harlequin removed his spectacles and sank back into his throne as he awaited a reaction from the tortoiseshell cat. After a little pause for thought the offender finally spoke up.

"This is ridiculous!" he squawked. "You can't make me do anything I don't want to do."

Harlequin shrugged his shoulders.

"The choice is yours," he said calmly. "It's up to you whether you wish to remain here as a cat or become human again. The spell is already cast and it cannot be undone... In the meantime, we need to give you a name."

"I'm sure that I already have a name, but for some reason I just can't remember what it is at the moment."

"That's because you are still in the transition period between human and feline," Harlequin informed him. "Allow me to remind you of your name: in the human world you were known as Thomas Benjamin Durrow…"

"Now I remember!"

"…but we need to change it."

"Why?"

"Well, for one thing, cats don't normally have more than one name."

"But I've had the same name for ten years. Humans are given a name when they're born and they usually keep it forever."

"You're not a person any more, you're a cat."

"How could I possibly forget?" the tortoiseshell sarcastically retorted.

"Good, it's finally sinking in."

"Okay, so I accept that I'm now a cat (for the moment at least), but why can't I keep my first name or even use my second name?"

"It's such a common name. There are too many cats called Thomas – it will become confusing – and Benjamin is too long. Can you imagine your owners calling out your name in the street when they're trying to get you to come in at night? No, I think not!"

"How about shortening my name to Tom?"

"Tom sounds too much like it should be a mouse's name."

"Well if that's the case, then what's wrong with Ben?"

"Ben is a rat's name – although that would probably be apt and fitting in your case."

"You could just use my surname instead," said the tortoiseshell ignoring Harlequin's comment.

"Durrow the cat? No, that title doesn't have a nice sound to it at all. Besides, cats don't have surnames… Gubbins, bring me the Hat of a Thousand Names please."

"Very good M'Lord," said Gubbins.

The Devon Rex quickly produced a black top hat from beneath the long table and positioned it upside down in front of Harlequin. The Catmaster then placed a large paw inside the upturned hat and began to rummage around. All of a sudden he stopped what he was doing and looked at Gubbins with a twinkle in his eye.

"I've just had a brainwave! I believe we should let our newest recruit to Catland choose his own name," announced Harlequin.

"What a splendid idea, M'lord," Gubbins agreed.

"Come forth young fellow and pick a name," said Harlequin beckoning the tortoiseshell towards him with a long claw.

With a certain amount of reservation the tortoiseshell slowly approached the wizardly Catmaster and his assistant who was now holding the hat aloft, the skinny face of the Devon Rex portraying an even more manic expression than ever before. He reached into the hat and delved around, eyeing Harlequin and Gubbins with some suspicion as he did so. All of a sudden he let out an exclamation of surprise as he withdrew a piece of paper.

"There's only one name in the hat!"

"Then it must be yours…" chanted Harlequin and Gubbins together.

"Ooh, it's so exciting," said Gubbins leaping around and turning cartwheels like a crazy lunatic. Then he quickly settled down and with an amused smile on his face and a wicked gleam in his eyes he said: "Come along now; don't keep us in suspense any longer. Open it up and let us know what it says."

The tortoiseshell unfolded the piece of paper before letting out another cry of astonishment.

"Well? The suspense is nearly killing us," squealed Gubbins clutching one paw to his heart and holding another paw over his eyes. "What are we to call you?"

"*IAN!*" uttered the tortoiseshell in disgust.

"Ah, such a nice name," said Harlequin in a dreamy voice.

"Yes, it's got a certain ring to it," Gubbins chimed in.

The tortoiseshell was aghast and his voice echoed his feelings as he dolefully repeated his name out loud for a second time.

"*IAN!* What kind of name is that for a cat? Who in their right mind would give such a stupid name to a cat?"

"WE WOULD!" chorused Harlequin The Catmaster and his gleeful assistant Gubbins.

"Why can't I be called something nice... something-y for instance? Loads of cats have names ending in Y; like Blacky, or Snowy, or Molly – No, that's a girl's name; don't you dare call me that."

"We wouldn't dream of doing such a thing. Mind you, on second thoughts..." said Gubbins with a wicked grin on his face.

"No, please don't!"

"It's alright, he's just kidding," laughed Harlequin. "We like the name Ian; it's got a certain amount of style about it, and we think that it suits you."

"Aw, come on... How about giving me another name; perhaps something different, such as Magic," the tortoiseshell pleaded. "Yes, that would be a cool name for a cat."

"NO!" Harlequin and Gubbins chanted in unison as they shook their heads from side to side. They were adamant.

"Ian it is," said Harlequin. "Make a note in your book please Magenta."

"But you cheated," complained the tortoiseshell. "You knew all along there was only one name in the hat and that I would be called Ian. It's not fair!"

"Life's not fair young fellow so we have to make the best of what we have: such as our names – IAN," Harlequin mused, holding his front paws out in front of him and shrugging his broad shoulders. "I don't know, things aren't going too well for you at present are they? Firstly you're turned into a loathsome cat and then you're given a name that you don't like. Whatever next?"

"Yeah, I dread to think what comes next," grumbled Ian the tortoiseshell cat.

"Well, for the time being, there is nothing next," announced Harlequin. "That's it; we've finished with you for now. You're free to go."

"Go where?"

"Out into the big wide world, of course."

"But where will I go?"

Harlequin shrugged his shoulders again.

"I don't know," he said, "you'll have to find somewhere to go."

"Hang on a minute," said Ian after a rather thoughtful period of time. "I seem to remember you mentioning something earlier about my owners calling out my name... Doesn't that mean I will have someone to look after me?"

"No."

"Why not? All cats have owners."

"You don't! You're a stray cat from now on and you will have to find an owner by using your own initiative," said Harlequin. "Oh, and by the way, I want you to report to me on a weekly basis without fail, and don't let me see you back in court again unless it's good news," warned Harlequin. "Now, do you have any final questions before you go?"

"No," grunted Ian sulkily, but then he had a change of heart. "Wait a second... Yeah, I do have a question actually. How long do I have to carry out these tasks or tests you're gonna give me?"

"Oh how silly of me. Do you know I hadn't really given that any thought at all, but now that you have mentioned it shall we say the time period will expire on Christmas Eve at midnight?" replied Harlequin with a playful sparkle in his eye.

"But it's nearly Christmas now," moaned Ian.

"Then I suggest you'd better pull your finger out if you want to return home for the festive season, hadn't you?" replied Harlequin unsympathetically. "And remember this: if you don't have any lives remaining at that time you will always be a tortoiseshell cat! Right, as far as I'm concerned that should just about cover everything for the time being... Good-bye and good luck. Please leave by the back door, there's a good chap."

"But…" Ian began to protest.

"Trojan, show our new friend out please," ordered Harlequin.

"It'll be a pleasure M'Lord," growled Trojan.

"On second thoughts you'd better show him out instead Spartan, because I need to have a quiet word with Trojan about bullying!"

Spartan nodded his head but still he said nothing.

"Oh, one more thing before you go," added Harlequin. He waved a large furry paw in front of Ian's face and instantly the tortoiseshell felt something tighten around his neck.

"What's this?" gasped Ian clutching at his throat. "It feels really uncomfortable."

"It's a collar containing nine amber crystals – you will soon get used to it. Every time you lose one of your nine lives a crystal will turn black and die but if you regain a life the crystal with re-ignite and glow brightly. There is also a medallion attached to the collar with your name etched on it so that everyone will know what your name is."

"You can't do this to me," grumbled Ian at the same time trying to tear off the collar.

"GOOD-BYE IAN," chanted Harlequin and Gubbins together.

Still protesting about everything and anything Ian was dragged away by Spartan, whose meaty paw had a firm grip on the tortoiseshell's new collar, and taken along a winding corridor to a doorway that was in effect a giant cat-flap. After being forced through it in no uncertain terms Ian found himself in another dark earthen tunnel with no access back to Catland because the cat-flap had mysteriously vanished without trace to leave him in yet another unknown place with only one direction in which to go.

CHAPTER FOUR

Ian the Cat
Meets Adolf the Dog

Ian didn't know where he was now. All he knew was that it was dark in the tunnel and quite smelly too, and the further he walked the worse the pong became. After a short while he found that the tunnel split in two directions and not knowing which route to follow Ian decided to take the left-hand fork. From then on he seemed to be travelling downhill, where the ground beneath him was becoming rather soggy, and the confused cat didn't like the effect underfoot at all because it made the fleshy pads on the bottom of his paws feel extremely cold and uncomfortable.

All of a sudden he lost his footing and began to slide. Frantically he flapped about, attempting to dig his claws into the sodden earth, but it was no good because the ground was becoming steeper and muddier, and then he finally lost his grip altogether. Downwards he slid, getting faster and faster all the while as he gathered momentum, until he shot out of an opening in the ground at what seemed like supersonic speed before landing face down in a pool of foul-smelling brown liquid tinged with ribbons of purple and green.

Slightly dazed Ian picked himself up, shook his matted fur that was now caked in some sort of evil-smelling gunge, and after wiping the dark, pungent stuff away from his eyes he looked all around him. As his eyes began to focus he realized that he was back out in the daylight and a relieved smile started to spread across his face. It was good to be outside again he thought, at the same time inhaling deeply in order to draw a huge breath of fresh air. But then he wished he hadn't taken such a deep breath because the awful stench was even stronger and it had a distinct odour of raw sewage about it. In the next instance Ian spotted a nearby farm partly hidden from his view by the steep slopes of Sunrise Hill where there was a large slurry pit close beside the river, and it suddenly dawned on him where he had ended up.

It was raw sewage!

He had just been ejected through a drainage pipe at the foot of Sunrise Hill that flowed into the slurry pit and now he was covered from head to foot in pooh – fresh, runny cow dung to be exact. He was now sitting slap-bang in the middle of this stinking pool and from where he was he could see the warning sign beside the pit and could even read the words that were written on it.

'DANGER!

KEEP OUT!

RISK OF SUFFOCATION'

That's what the sign said, and he was definitely suffocating alright! Ian had always wondered where the mysterious pipe led that was poking out of Sunrise Hill above the slurry pit and now he knew because it turned out to be the emergency exit from Catland. But how he wished he hadn't discovered where the pipe went because now he stank to high heaven.

Luckily the slurry pit was quite shallow so Ian managed to wade to solid ground where he sat down wondering what he needed to do to get rid of the disgusting pooh that had stuck to his fur like chewing gum sticks in a human's hair. It soon became apparent that he only had one option open to him.

"Oh, well," he grumbled out loud. "There's nothing else for it because it has to be done…"

With that he began to wash himself, and when he licked his fur he found out that cow pooh tasted as awful as it smelled and made the poor cat feel extremely sick; however, cats have a much higher tolerance to such things than humans do and very soon he was clean again. With the terrible task complete he was then ready to set off and find himself a home.

Ian realized that if he followed the river in the direction that it flowed it would eventually take him to a bridge that crossed over to the far river-bank. From there he only had to walk a short distance along a lane that led into the small town where his family lived and then he would just turn up at the front door. But were they likely to recognize him now that he was a cat, he wondered? And would they let him into the house? Well, his family certainly wouldn't recognize him – he knew that – but his sister loved cats so he was full of hope at the thought of being allowed indoors. Ellie had always wanted a cat of her own, therefore her wish was about to come true.

"Huh!" thought Ian. "How stupid Harlequin must be to think I was going to be homeless and that nobody would want to take me in. I'll show him, and then we'll see who's really clever."

By the time Ian arrived in the street where his family lived it was nightfall. He strutted casually beneath the streetlamps with his tail held high in the air, pleased as punch that he would soon be home and tucked up in (or at least on) his old bed. But when he got to the front door of Number 9 Catkin Mews the house was in complete darkness.

"Where could they be?" he wondered. "My family never go out at night. Maybe they're asleep – I'll try and wake them up."

At the top of his voice he meowed, screeched and wailed, making the most hideous sound he had ever heard, let alone anyone else had ever heard. But howl as he may there was still no sign of life at his family home, although he did manage to disturb the neighbouring household. After a couple of minutes of constant wailing every single light at Number 10 shone out through the windows of the house and an upstairs bedroom window was immediately flung open. Then Mr Johnson's angry face appeared in the opening.

"Go away you pesky animal," shouted Mr Johnson. "Go on, be off with you… Shoo!"

Ian stayed put. He was determined to wake up his own family, so he continued with his mournful wailings. Meanwhile, Mr Johnson briefly disappeared, returning just a few seconds later with a bucket full of water that he raised into the air before flinging its contents in the direction of the inharmonious crooner. With lightning reflexes Ian leapt out of the way leaving the water to splash harmlessly onto the front lawn where he had previously been sitting.

"There, that shut you up didn't it?" yelled Mr Johnson. "Now, maybe I can get some sleep."

Having said his piece and quite satisfied that the cat would go away, Mr Johnson shut the bedroom window and the house returned to darkness when he turned off the lights.

Ian was fuming.

"I could have drowned!" he muttered. "Didn't like my singing huh? The cheek of the man... Right, that's it! I'll teach him to throw water at me."

With purpose in his step, embarking on a mission to wreak revenge, the irritable cat wound his way around the house to the rear garden where he plonked himself down on Mr Johnson's patio. Then he cleared his throat and began to wail incessantly again, this time even louder than before. Instantly the house became illuminated once more when the lights were switched on for the second time. A bright outdoor spotlight came on too, lighting up a large section of the patio area. Then Ian heard the sound of a key being turned in the lock of the patio door.

"Ooh, I'd better hide in the shadows behind that rose bush so that he can't see me when he comes out," thought Ian, chuckling away to himself. "I don't want to have another bucket of water thrown at me because the next shot might be on target."

Ian dived for cover just as the patio door was thrown wide open.

"Go get him boy," were the next words he heard Mr Johnson say.

Suddenly the smile disappeared from Ian's face and the fur on Ian's body immediately began to stand on end, partly through fright and partly to make him appear more scary to the opponent he was about to encounter.

"Oh... My... Gosh!" Ian panicked. "I had completely forgotten about Adolf the dog."

Adolf was a breed of dog known as a Doberman Pincer and he hated cats. Only a short while ago, when Ian was a boy living next door to Mr Johnson, he had watched the dog see off many an intruding cat from his territory often with painful results for the poor moggy involved. How he had laughed when he had previously witnessed these cat chasings but now the tables were turned around and he was about to be on the receiving end of Adolf's sharp gnashers.

"Perhaps he'll know who I am," thought Ian hopefully. "Oh, how stupid – I'm a cat now, how could he possibly know that I used to be the boy next door?"

After a few seconds of watching the dog aimlessly tearing around the garden in an attempt to locate the now silent cat Ian decided to make a break for it. But as soon as Ian began to move Adolf instantly picked up his scent and he quickly spotted the retreating cat. The black and tan missile launched itself across the lawn, snarling ominously and bearing a full set of rather nasty-looking fangs, his fierce eyes glowing a shade of bright red beneath the powerful outdoor spotlight. Taking a defensive stance Ian arched his back, squinted his eyes into narrow slits and turned his ears backwards until they almost lay flat against his head; however, as menacing as he might try to appear, he knew that he was going to be no match for the powerful brute of a dog that was about to rip him to shreds with his mighty jaws.

But just at the moment when Ian thought his number was about to be up Adolf suddenly stopped dead. He had ceased to growl, retracted his teeth and a puzzled expression was written all over his face. It turned out that the dog had become quickly confused because he had indeed picked up a scent but it was the scent of a human boy and not that of a cat, for although he had been transformed into an animal there would still be a human odour until all nine lives were lost and the transformation was complete.

"Huh?" said Adolf, sitting down and cocking his head to one side. "There's something wrong here. Ya smell like the obnoxious brat that used to live next door."

"Then you do recognize me!" exclaimed Ian. "Oh, thank the Lord."

"Yeah… Er? No. I dunno, I'm kinda mixed up at the moment," replied the Doberman. "I see a cat, but I recognize the smell of a boy."

"That's because I am the boy next door – and a cat too. It's a long story… What do you mean *used* to live next door?"

"Moved away, so they did. The boy simply vanished and his mom and sis went away. Went on holiday I hear."

"Went on holiday? My family have never been on holiday in their lives – we couldn't afford to. I've always wanted to go on holiday… And now you're telling me that they've gone without me?"

Ian was devastated. He had always been jealous of his friends when they went on holiday and now he felt envious of his family, annoyed, and upset that they had gone without him. A great sadness overcame him at the thought of this and tears began to roll down Ian's cheeks. Adolf felt equally bad for Ian and his face drooped whilst tears welled up in his eyes too. For a few moments the two animals sat in mournful silence until they were disturbed when an angry voice could be heard coming from the doorway of the house.

"ADOLF! What the heck is the matter with you, you dumb mutt?"

"You're not going to let him speak to you like that are you?" asked Ian snapping out of his sorrowful state.

"He's my master. He always speaks to me like that, and he talks to his missus in just the same way," replied Adolf. "He's not really a polite man at all. Got no respect, that's his problem... Bit like the kid next door".

"Hey, watch it, that's me you're talking about..."

"Sorry, but the truth always hurts mate."

"I don't want to hear about it... Aren't you going to do anything about the way your master talks to you? Like, bite him or something?"

"One thing you learn in this life mate is to never bite the hand that feeds you. I know which side my bread is buttered on."

"Someone else said a similar thing to me recently," said Ian, "but I don't care who I hurt so long as I get what I want."

"HEY, PEA BRAIN! You're supposed to get rid of that flamin' cat, not sit and dance with it. Some killer dog you turned out to be," ranted Mr Johnson.

"Sorry Son, you're gonna have to go. I've gotta save face a bit and chase ya outta the garden now. No offence like."

"None taken… What do you want me to do?"

"Hiss an' squawk a lot. You know, make some horrible noises like ya did before."

"I was singing actually!"

"You were?" said Adolf in genuine surprise. "Oh, I'm sorry, I didn't realize. Anyway, forget about that – act like you're scared stiff and run for your life, that's all ya gotta do. You know; do the usual sort of stuff that cats do when a dog chases them."

"You're not going to hurt me though, are you?"

"No, of course not."

"Okay, I'll do my best, but give me a head start won't you? I'm new to this game."

"I'll count to three… One – Two – Three; coming, ready or not," barked the Doberman.

Like a scalded cat, Ian had already taken off and he was heading for the nearest fence.

"ATTA BOY ADOLF! That's more like it," yelled Mr Johnson admiringly, clasping his hands together joyfully as he watched his huge muscular hound chasing the scrawny little cat across the garden.

By the time Ian reached the fence Adolf had gained on him and he could already hear the drooling, slavering jaws of the dog close behind him as well as feeling his hot fiery breath on his furry tail. Panicking all the while he launched himself skywards and, as he did so, Adolf snapped his teeth together, ripping a portion of fur from Ian's rear end. Having landed safely on top of the fence the cat then clambered onto the flat surface of a fence post where he would be well out of reach from Adolf's clutches before beginning to examine the damage to his posterior.

"Ouch! That's really sore," Ian complained in a pitiful voice. "I thought you weren't going to hurt me. Did you have to do that? Now I probably won't be able to sit down for at least a week."

"Sorry mate, but I had to make it look good. Got a reputation to keep up, you know," spluttered Adolf as he spat out a mouthful of fur. "Man, that tasted disgusting… like you've been through a sewer or something."

"Yeah? Well, I have actually. I thought I'd got rid of all the muck though," muttered Ian.

"Not a good day for you really, is it?" said Adolf trying his hardest not to laugh at the cat's misfortunes.

"It certainly seems that way," moaned Ian in a dreary voice.

"Never mind, it can only get better," Adolf encouraged. "But remember, things usually get worse before they improve."

"Great! Thanks for telling me," said Ian sarcastically.

"Good work Boy, now finish him off," interrupted Mr Johnson.

"Oh for goodness sake, give it a rest will ya," mumbled Adolf. "Do me a favour Sonny: when I jump up at you, fall off the other side of the fence and skedaddle will ya, otherwise he'll be on my case all night long."

"I don't see why I should. I mean, you've bitten me so you haven't done me any favours have you?" said Ian adopting his usual selfish attitude again now that he was out of harm's way.

"Aw, come on, be reasonable. I coulda chewed you to bits in this garden, and ya know it. Sometimes you have to be unselfish and help out others who have tried to help you."

"I ain't budging, pal. I want to see what your owner does to punish you. Look after Number One, that's what I always say – It's a dog-eat-dog world."

"It'll be a dog-eat-flippin'-cat world if ya ever step paw inside this garden again," warned Adolf. "That sort of attitude sucks. No wonder you haven't got any friends or family."

As soon as he had finished saying his piece Adolf launched himself at the fence with all his might whereupon the tremendous weight and force of the Doberman's powerful, muscular body caused the wooden structure to shake violently. Ian was taken by surprise when the fence shook as he nonchalantly licked his paws and ignored Adolf's words, which caused him to fall off the fence post, his claws making a loud scratching sound as he painfully tried to attach himself to the wooden panels on the way down in an attempt to slow down his descent. The cat's frantic scrambling made no difference whatsoever though because he crashed heavily to the ground and landed on his already sore backside which made him meow and scream in agony.

"He won't be back in a hurry," laughed Mr Johnson as he listened to Ian's pathetic squealing coming from the other side of the fence.

"Come on, Boy, let's go back indoors; you deserve a treat for getting rid of that dreadful animal."

"Good luck Son, I think you're gonna need it," Adolf barked through the fence at Ian. "...And don't come back here again or you'll be sorry."

Having had the final word Adolf the dog turned to follow his master, for although Mr Johnson often spoke to his faithful friend in a rather nasty manner Adolf was a loyal companion who knew he would always be justly rewarded for his obedience.

CHAPTER FIVE

A Brief Spell in Catland

Nursing his extremely sore behind and freshly torn claws Ian stole quietly into the night searching for a place to stay. The weather had unexpectedly taken a turn for the worse and it had developed into a stormy night with strong gusts of wind that spooked Ian every time a piece of debris blew past him or a branch snapped from a tree sending it crashing to the ground with a hollow thudding sound. Then it began to rain, and very soon his short tortoiseshell fur became drenched until it could absorb no more rainwater. In no time at all the driving weather had penetrated his coat and was hitting his skin as if ice-cold needles were being deliberately prodded into him. Now he knew the true meaning of being soaked to the skin, and he had also discovered that cats hate rain because their fur is thick and warm but it is certainly not waterproof.

On several occasions Ian would discover what he thought was a suitable place to shelter but whenever he did it would already be occupied by another cat who promptly told him to clear off and look for a place of his own. As a last resort the only vacant spot he could eventually find was beneath a park bench where the open slats of the seat gave very little shelter from the driving rain. This was better than nothing at all so the exhausted cat settled down for what little remained of the night.

Having snoozed for only a short period of time the unfortunate cat was disturbed by the chirping of dozens of birds that always arose at dawn, but at least it had stopped raining. Feeling cold, soggy and irritable Ian got to his feet, stretched his aching body and yawned the most enormous yawn. The day had only just begun but already he felt tired, and he was very hungry too. Having spent only one night in feline form he had already made up his mind that he hated being a cat because it didn't seem to be much fun at all, and with this thought in his head he decided to pay Harlequin a visit to see whether The Catmaster would transform him back into a boy again.

Ian made his way back towards Catland following the course of the river until he arrived at the foot of Sunrise Hill where in the early light of day he could see the great white oak looming out of the mist that rolled off the river. The formidable tree seemed even taller now that he was a cat but he thought that it would at least be easier to climb because he could dig his claws into the tough bark and pull himself up with little effort. He had seen cats climb trees in the past at lightning speed and they made it look so easy, therefore there was no apparent reason why he couldn't do it. But, at the very moment he stretched out his limbs to place his front paws on the tree, a pair of wooden shutters were flung open and the head of a red squirrel appeared through a hole in the trunk. Then the faces of yet more squirrels popped out of little arched windows at various intervals.

"So that's what those hand and footholds are," muttered Ian in surprise. "They're look-out posts!"

"What do you want?" demanded the first squirrel that had poked its head out of a tree window.

"I've come to see Harlequin," Ian boldly replied.

"Hang on a minute, let me just check my diary," said the squirrel, and it briefly vanished back inside the tree.

"You're not on our visitors' list today," announced the squirrel when it reappeared. "In fact, you're not due to report to The Catmaster until next week."

"But I have to see him right away."

"If you need to see The Catmaster you must make an appointment."

"Then I'll make an appointment to see him now," Ian cheekily replied.

"He's not free until next week, so it's pointless."

"What? So why did you ask me to make an appointment you stupid creature? This gets more and more ridiculous all the time," Ian angrily retorted. "Whether you like it or not, I'm climbing the tree."

"We are the guardians of the tree… Get back, or you'll be sorry!" warned the squirrel.

Ian took no notice whatsoever of the squirrel's warning and he defiantly began to climb the great white oak. Immediately that he did so, the red squirrel army produced the only weapon they possessed which they poked out of their tiny tree windows and took aim. Then they fired their miniature catapults at the insolent cat and launched a barrage of large, dried acorns upon him. The bombardment of acorns

58

pelted the tortoiseshell cat hitting their target on his nose, on top of his head and just about every part of his anatomy, until the unsuspecting animal was forced to hurriedly retreat to ground level.

"Yeeow! Meeow! Greeow!" Ian yelped in pain as the shower of acorns rained down on him. "Come on guys, please let me see The Catmaster," he pleaded.

"We're not guys, we're girls actually," the squirrel informed him. "And, no, you can't see The Catmaster – I've already told you."

At this point Ian gave up trying, knowing that the red squirrels were not going to let him enter Catland no matter what. Dragging his tail between his legs Ian skulked away from the tree, muttering unrepeatable oaths under his breath as he went. Suddenly though, a thought crossed his mind and he began to brighten up when he recalled the rear entrance to Catland near to the slurry pit.

"If there's a back door that comes out of Catland and the tree entrance is guarded by squirrels, then there has to be another way in," he pondered.

With that in mind he set off, heading in the opposite direction to the river and following a route that took him around the base of Sunrise Hill. Very soon Ian came across the entrance to a disused mineshaft, although it was barricaded with a large grey stone slab.

"This looks promising," thought Ian, "but how do I get in?"

He pushed the slab, pulled at it, kicked it, and even pressed his paw against it in several places in the hope that there was a pressure point of some kind, but try as he may the huge lump of stone wasn't budging.

"I must be missing something, or maybe it's not an entrance after all," puzzled Ian as he sat down on the ground and eyed the stone in frustration, trying his best to figure out a way in.

Just then he heard voices – cat voices – and they were getting ever nearer. Worried that he would be spotted trying to enter the kingdom of Catland Ian frantically glanced around for somewhere to hide and, fortunately, he espied a clump of gorse nearby. It was the closest and only object suitable enough to cover him so he quickly leapt into the bush. The prickly gorse needles passed through Ian's fur before piercing his skin and he desperately wanted to move away from the uncomfortable bed of needles but he didn't dare because two cats had now come into view. He recognized them too: they were none other than Spartan and Trojan, the two ginger sentries that had led him to and from the courtroom. They stopped beside the stone slab warily looking about them to make sure they weren't being watched and when the animals were positive that it was safe to do so Ian heard Spartan say the magic word.

"Abra-CAT-abra!"

Ian could have kicked himself. "Why didn't I think of using a password? How simple and how very obvious", he whispered quietly as he watched the stone begin to move to reveal its hidden entrance.

With a grating sound the huge stone slid aside and the two cats stepped into a dark hole in the hillside before the mineshaft entrance closed up behind them. When he was sure the coast was clear Ian finally came out of his hiding place, delicately plucking the numerous gorse needles from his flesh that were causing him a great deal of discomfort by now. This took quite some time to achieve because there were so many of them, but when he was finally needle-free Ian approached the stone.

"Abra-CAT-abra!" he chanted, and his heart leapt with joy when the huge stone moved aside to reveal the entrance once again.

Once he was safely inside the hillside the stone slab closed shut behind him sealing the opening from the outside world. But now there was another dilemma to contend with because it appeared that the grassy slopes of Sunrise Hill disguised a catacomb of old mining tunnels and Ian didn't know which one he should take.

The first tunnel he chose brought him back to the point where he had originally set out from after a wasted half-hour hike, and so did the second. Then he tried a third tunnel, and in no time at all Ian became hopelessly lost. It was just like a maze and every direction he took finished with a dead-end, so he was left with no choice but to retrace his steps to try and get back to the entrance of the catacomb. It took an age but eventually, purely through luck and determination, the relieved cat managed to return to his starting point.

By now Ian was at his wits end and, covered in dust from some of the tight squeezes he had encountered on his travels, he flopped down wearily onto the ground and began to wash his coat. During one particularly long sweep of his tongue a mouthful of fur got caught up (as so often happens when cats preen themselves) and he raised his head in an attempt to separate his rough tongue from the tangled fur. It was only then that Ian realized his mistake, for there, just above his head, he spotted a wrought-iron cat ladder and he felt so stupid because it was all so obvious… the entrance would at one time have been the main shaft of the mine and miners would have had to gain access to other levels above this one in the hillside.

He immediately stopped preening his coat, grabbed hold of the cat ladder and climbed upwards until he could go no further because his head had come into contact with a metal hatch. The hatch turned out to be a giant magnetic cat-flap that hinged on one end and opened away from him as Ian pushed gently against it and clambered through the opening. Finally he had made it back into Catland.

Ian now found himself in a well-lit corridor with several doors leading off it. The first door he approached had a copper plaque attached to it with two words etched into its shiny surface in large print and three smaller words beneath it which read:

SPELL ROOM
PRIVATE – KEEP OUT

And those last three words were the very thing that tempted him to enter because if something was forbidden then it was right up his street and in his eyes he was the very person who was fully qualified to investigate the matter further.

After opening the door Ian found himself in a quaint little room that was well stocked with books – old books in general – mostly covered in thick dust, with a strange musty smell about them that told you they were ancient. Ian's curiosity quickly got the better of him and he began to flick lazily through some of the almanacs to see what they contained. It turned out they were all spell books that contained a magic spell for just about every occasion. There were recipes for changing the weather from rain to sunshine; or how to turn someone poor into someone rich; or how to make an ugly person into a beautiful one. It was all there in black and white – the answers to all of the World's problems! And there were even separate spells for males and females.

The books were very delicate and many of the pages had come loose because of their great age, which gave Ian the wicked idea of jumbling them up so that whoever cast the spells would get things totally mixed up. Without hesitation the mischievous cat began to swap the loose pages around.

"There should be some interesting results from this," chuckled Ian when he had finished and as he was placing the worn almanacs back where they belonged.

With this task done his attention then turned elsewhere. He noticed that there were shelves full of pots and pans brimming with herbs and spices and several cabinets within the room were full of jars that housed strange ingredients necessary for the making of spells. They contained bat wings, frogs' eyes, rabbit tails, fish scales and badger claws, amongst others. In fact, all manner of creature were represented in the numerous jars.

"Huh! And Harlequin says that I'm cruel to animals," muttered Ian as he studied the animal parts in disgust.

Next he spotted an assortment of laboratory apparatus bubbling merrily away upon a gas stove in a dark corner of the room. The brightly-coloured liquid contents held within the glass apparatus gave off a strange glow and Ian didn't even dare to hazard a guess as to what it consisted of, therefore (unusually for him) he left it well alone.

The final item that was of interest to Ian was a highly-polished copper cauldron (so big that it was large enough to hold a cow) which took pride of place in the centre of the room. Ian struggled to clamber onto a slippery ceramic work-surface so that he could peer into the depths of the deep cauldron only to discover that it was empty except for a small sheepskin rug that had deliberately been positioned at the bottom of it. This looked extremely inviting and feeling quite tired from his day's adventure the intrepid explorer jumped into the cauldron where he curled up on the warm sheepskin to take a catnap. But Ian's slumber was short-lived when he was disturbed by the sound of a familiar voice.

"You can come out now," said Harlequin.

Ian opened his eyes and cringed but he remained put, pretending that it was all a dream and he hadn't really been discovered.

"Shall I go and fetch Trojan, M'Lord?" asked Gubbins playfully.

The very thought of this terrible threat made Ian spring to his feet. He stretched his long body, putting his front paws on the rim of the copper cauldron, and then he revealed his guilty impish features to The Catmaster and his faithful assistant Gubbins.

"What are you doing in here?" asked Harlequin.

"Trying to get some sleep," Ian cheekily replied.

Harlequin and Gubbins exchanged long-suffering glances but said nothing.

"I thought I'd just pop in for a spell," joked Ian. "Spell – get it? A short period of time… Oh never mind. Well, the sign did say 'Spell

Room' on the door – R-O-O-M – there; I've spelt the word 'room' for you, just like the sign said!"

Ian began to laugh his socks off whilst the two wizard cats continued to stare at one another in complete bewilderment.

"You're not at all funny, you know. Perhaps you should leave the jokes to us," groaned Harlequin when Ian began to settle down. "Now that you've had your moment of fame I'll rephrase the question... How did you get in here?"

"Through the door," said Ian and he erupted into fits of laughter again.

Even Gubbins began to snigger at this, but the assistant wizard quickly stifled his laughter as The Catmaster rolled his eyes in disgust and angrily growled at Ian.

"Okay, enough is enough; it's obvious I'm not going to get a straight answer out of you. However, I think I know how to get your attention. You were distinctly told by Cerise the squirrel that you weren't allowed into Catland today and for such disobedience YOU WILL LOSE A LIFE!"

Harlequin waved his hefty furry paws in the air and Ian heard a loud 'PHUT-PHUT, FIZZ!' sound close to his ears. Instantly one of the amber crystals on the tortoiseshell's collar turned black. A brief look of concern showed in the expression on his face, but he quickly shrugged this off.

"I've got plenty more," he boasted.

"And now, for the way you treated Adolf the dog when he tried to help you, YOU MUST LOSE YOUR SECOND LIFE!"

Once again Harlequin waved his paws frantically about. This was followed by another 'PHUT-PHUT, FIZZ!', and a second amber crystal faded out.

"Whoops! There goes another one," remarked the remorseless tortoiseshell.

"And for showing such lack of remorse…" Harlequin began to rant.

"Calm down M'Lord," Gubbins interrupted in a concerned voice. "I think you are being a little bit harsh."

"What? Oh yes, quite… Sorry Gubbins," said The Catmaster. "I got a little carried away there for a moment."

Harlequin nervously adjusted his hat and then his spectacles before clearing his throat and continuing to address Ian.

"Right, there's a lot to be done this afternoon. I haven't got any more time to waste on you at the moment, therefore I shall now send you…"

But Harlequin stopped what he was saying in mid-sentence and remained poised on the spot with his front paws raised in the air, his eyes rolling about in his head as if he was taking in his surroundings.

"You haven't touched anything in here, have you?" he worriedly asked.

"No, of course not," replied Ian with a wicked glint in his eyes. "Would I do such a thing?"

"Nothing, it seems, is beyond you," answered Harlequin. "Do you promise me that you haven't touched anything in here?"

"I promise," said Ian.

"Hmm!" drawled The Catmaster doubtfully. "I'm glad to hear it because I have an important spell to cast very shortly when I shall be sending a gypsy cat on to better things. In fact, I think you met the very fellow in the Limbo Room while you were awaiting sentence yesterday. You would know him as Phillip."

"Oh yes, I remember him. I thought he would have already gone from here by now though."

"I gave him a brief one-day holiday; he deserved it after passing all of his tests," replied The Catmaster. "Anyway, enough of this idle chit-chat, it's time for you to disappear too young Ian."

"Do I have to leave by the front door or the back door?" said Ian trying to climb out of the slippery copper cauldron.

Neither! Stay exactly where you are because I shall send you packing from this very spot... And don't forget to come by and see me next week."

Harlequin raised his paws into the air as he poised himself to cast the vanishing spell.

"No, please allow me M'Lord," Gubbins quickly interrupted again. With that, he waved his bony limbs and Ian instantly disappeared from the cauldron.

"You shouldn't let him get to you, Harlequin," said Gubbins in a soothing voice after Ian had vanished.

"You know Gubbins, I've don't think I've ever had anyone quite so difficult before," replied The Catmaster.

"We have never lost any of our subjects in the past, so I don't see why there should be a serious problem with this one," Gubbins reassured him.

"All the same I'm concerned because this boy is different. He's extremely hard work, but I will stick with it because I'm convinced that the lad has some potential. What worries me is that he has only been a cat for a day and already he's lost two lives; I'd hate to see him lose all of them, especially in such a short space of time."

"It could be the only way the youngster will learn. Don't forget that he's here to be taught a valuable lesson about morals," Gubbins reminded him. "However, I do agree with you that he is a very difficult child. Perhaps he needs a little guidance with his quest."

"You mean…"

"Yes Harlequin, he could do with a guardian angel… a Permanent Cat."

"Do you have a particular cat in mind?" asked The Catmaster.

"Leave it with me, I believe I know just the cat for the job. And it's a she-cat – that will really annoy him."

Harlequin thoughtfully stroked the long blue-grey fur around his face.

"Yes my dear fellow, a fine idea indeed. It may just be what the little monster needs."

CHAPTER SIX

It's not Easy Being a Cat

Having been evicted from Catland for a second time, Ian the cat rematerialized amidst the stinking pool of slurry beside the river.

"Gross!" he grumbled in an irritated voice. "Trust them to magic me out here, I could have saved them the bother and done it myself."

"It's not easy being a cat, is it?" said a soft, sweet sounding voice behind him that almost made Ian jump a mile.

Ian looked all around him, but he could not see anyone and neither could he tell where the voice was coming from.

"Uh? Who said that?" he asked out loud, at the same time wondering whether he had imagined hearing the mystery voice.

"I did," was the reply, followed by a giggle.

Again Ian looked all around him and this time he spotted a chocolate and cream coloured Birman cat perched elegantly upon the end of the sewer outlet. With her huge almond-shaped sapphire blue eyes that defined her perfectly-formed cheekbones, she was the most beautiful vision he had seen since he had been transformed into a cat, and Ian imagined that if he was a real cat there would be no doubt that she would be the one for him.

"Wow!" he exclaimed in a moment of weakness. Then he cleared his throat and in a surly manner he added: "What do you want?"

The Birman cat ignored his icy attitude towards her.

"Pooh! You are in a bit of a mess aren't you Ian? And in more ways than one," she remarked.

"How do you know my name?" he asked rather abruptly.

"Everyone in Catland knows your name Ian."

"Don't call me Ian, I hate that name."

"Then what shall I call you?"

"I don't know, just don't call me Ian."

"How about Stinky? That sounds like a fitting name for you because you really do stink quite a bit."

"No, don't call me that either!"

"Too late, I'm going to call you Stinky from now on."

"Look, I'm not interested in talking to you, whoever you are," snapped Ian. "Go away and leave me alone."

"Okay, if that's what you wish," said the Birman rising to her feet and stretching her slender, slinky body. "But before I go, I would just like to mention that there is a chance you may well need something to keep you warm… I rescued that thing for you when you splashed down in the slurry and I placed it on the dry ground over there."

Ian glanced towards the spot where the Birman was pointing with a well-groomed paw whereupon he noticed that the sheepskin rug that had lain in the bottom of the cauldron had been transported with him when he was expelled from Catland. With a look of surprise on his face he turned around to say something else to the Birman cat but she had already disappeared.

The tortoiseshell cat laboriously trudged out of the slurry pit, which seemed slightly deeper today than it was previously, and it was more of a struggle to pull his body free. Eventually though he settled down on solid ground and licked his fur until it was clean again, grimacing and retching all the while because the cow pooh tasted even worse than it did the first time around. Trying to take his mind off what he was doing, Ian puzzled over the mysterious cat wondering who she was, where she came from and how she could so easily vanish into thin air like she did. When he had finished his necessary but repulsive task he grasped the sheepskin rug between his teeth and, ungratefully, dropped it into the river before setting out on his quest for a place to stay. Then he thought no more about his brief encounter with the beautiful Birman.

Later that same afternoon Ian found himself roaming around a neighbourhood where he had not previously visited whilst in his human form. It was a particularly affluent part of the town and anyone who was classed as rich lived in this area. The houses were all detached properties of ample proportions and more often than not they were surrounded by vast gardens, so because Ian was passing through the vicinity he decided to take a peek and see how the other half lived. So far, this was the only advantage he had found about being a cat – he had the freedom to come and go as he pleased and nobody batted an eyelid because he was just a cat. And that's what cats did as far as people thought: they trespassed in people's gardens, but then, much to the owner's annoyance, they had the cheek to dig a hole in their prize vegetable plot or in an area where they had just planted some flower seeds and use it as a toilet!

And Ian was not about to discontinue this age-old tradition because, when he had almost crossed the lawn of the tenth house that he was about to nose around, he was suddenly caught short. Desperate to go to the lavatory he excavated a small toilet hole in a flower bed close to a conservatory that was attached to the house, before readying himself into a squatting position and proceeding to use his newly-built toilet facility. With a concentrated yet blissful expression upon his face he closed his eyes until the job was done and when he opened them again he became aware of another cat staring at him from the conservatory window. Ian felt quite embarrassed by this.

"Huh! Is there no privacy?" he grumbled out loud, at the same time going about the task of covering his self-made toilet with loose soil.

The cat who had been staring at him didn't seem at all bothered about Ian's toilet escapade because it was a natural function after all. However, it did appear to be trying to get his attention by tapping on the glass window of the conservatory and beckoning him towards it. Ian could also hear the cat's muffled voice, although only vaguely, because there were air vents in the lower parts of the window frames that allowed sound to travel through them.

"Come over here," said the cat in quite a squeaky voice.

"Who, me?" asked Ian looking all around him.

"Who else could I mean, you fool? Apart from me you're the only other cat here!"

"There's no need to be funny, you posh git," Ian retorted as he took a defensive stance.

"I wasn't trying to be funny... Don't you recognize me?"

"Should I?"

"No, I guess you wouldn't... It's me... Phillip."

"Phillip? I don't know anyone called Phillip."

"Yes you do. I'm the cat you recently met in the Limbo Room in Catland."

"Oh, that Phillip! But you don't look anything like him," said Ian, eyeing the other cat rather suspiciously.

"That's because I've been transformed."

"Well, if I'd have been you, I would have kept your old shape Mate. What happened to you; you look all ponsified now?"

"That's just the problem. Why do you think I called you over?"

"I dunno. Why did you call me over?"

"Because I need your help, Soup for Brains! You see, it appears that the spell has gone horribly wrong somewhere along the line. Let me explain: I was supposed to be sent to another address on the other side of town (Pussywillow House in Coalpit Road to be exact) to some poor old guy who is really old and lonely, but I've ended up here instead."

"Huh, I don't know what you're worried about 'cos it looks to me as if you've got it made," said Ian scornfully as he jealously stared at the magnificent house.

73

"No, you don't understand, let me finish… I was supposed to be transformed with the same old body form that I had before – you know, the black long-haired common variety (I liked that one) – but instead of that I've become a pathetic pedigree Persian thingy with a squashed-up face and weird-coloured fur. Now I look as if I've had a purple rinse of some sort! And what's more, I'm a flippin' house cat who's being pampered to death by my new owners… It's a disaster!"

"Oh dear, it's not looking good is it?" said Ian trying to put on a sympathetic voice and stifle a laugh at the same time.

"It gets worse…" Phillip continued. "They've called me Lulabelle of all things! Now I'm a flippin' tomcat trapped in a female cat's body and I can't do anything about it."

Ian suddenly burst out laughing.

"It's not funny, you know," said the confused Persian rather indignantly. "They could have called me Phillippa or Pippa or something like that… at least those names are more similar to Phillip than Lulabelle is."

"I'm not laughing at that, I was actually laughing at the fact you're neither male nor female any more. Now I know why you are talking in such a high-pitched voice one minute and then a much deeper voice in the next," Ian managed to say between giggles.

"I told you, it's not funny!" snapped the Persian.

"Sorry," said Ian, but he couldn't stop laughing and he wasn't really sorry at all because it was his fault that poor Phillip had ended up this way. He new full well that if he hadn't muddled with the spell books when he was in Catland then Phillip would undoubtedly be living a much happier way of life right now.

"Please help me," begged the sorrowful Persian.

"What do you expect me to do about it?" asked the remorseless tortoiseshell, shamefully trying to appear innocent.

"You could do me a favour by returning to Catland and informing The Catmaster of this hideous error, if you wouldn't mind."

"I'll see if I can fit it into my agenda, I'm a little bit busy at the moment trying to find somewhere to stay."

"I don't want to put you out at all," replied the Persian sarcastically. "I mean, it's alright for you because you're still you – but I don't know who, or what, I am right now."

"It's not easy being a cat, is it?" Ian said casually. He had heard this phrase used by the female cat he had met earlier in the day and it sounded kind of cool so he thought he would use it again.

"You're still a beginner and you've got a lot to learn yet, what do you know about being a cat? At least you're free to roam, I'm not! Please, please, have a word with The Catmaster for me," pleaded Phillip the Persian.

"Alright, alright, don't go on about it. I'll see what I can do."

"Thanks," said Phillip, "I'll be most grateful if you would. By the way, what name did they give you in the end?"

"Ian."

"IAN?!!" screeched Phillip questioningly.

"Yes, that's what I said wasn't it? IAN!" he retorted defensively. "It's almost as bad as Phillip, isn't it?"

"Actually, I quite like the name Phillip."

"Then maybe you'll get used to being a female cat called Lulabelle too… or an inbetweeny – whatever you are."

75

"I don't believe I will ever get used to being Lulabelle. I'm neither male nor female now you know."

"Whatever! Anyway, I haven't got time to stand around talking any more 'cos I've gotta go now. I've got things to do and places to find," said Ian. He was becoming quite bored with the conversation by this time.

"Okay, I understand," agreed the muddled Persian. "It was nice to see you again though."

"Yeah, I know it was… and it was lucky for you that I was snooping around this neighbourhood or else nobody would have known you were here."

"Thanks again. I'm most grateful to you that you're going to see Harlequin The Catmaster, and that you will get him to put things right."

"Yeah… er, no problem," said Ian. "See ya."

With that, Ian walked away and departed from the garden of the large, posh house. However, he had no intention of going to see Harlequin because there were more pressing matters for him to attend to as far as he was concerned.

CHAPTER SEVEN

A New Home at Last

Just before dusk Ian arrived in Coalpit Road, an area that he knew extremely well because it had been one of his favourite haunts when he had been a human boy. It was a poor neighbourhood consisting of a small housing estate with very few dwellings, therefore Ian presumed that it wouldn't take him too long to locate the old man whose home Phillip should have been transported to and he would soon have somewhere permanent to live. By the time darkness fell the weary cat had patrolled the street thoroughly and, to his disgust, all of the houses he had nosed around so far contained either large families or single parents because this was the only place where they could afford to live.

He was just beginning to think that Phillip had got the name of the street wrong when he spotted a tiny cottage of shabby appearance that stood back from the road slightly. A rather worn out sign that was likely to have the house name on it hung precariously from the porch but the lettering was so weathered Ian couldn't read what it said. Ian was puzzled by the cottage because he couldn't remember seeing this particular building during previous visits to the housing estate although it stood out from the others, but all the same he decided to investigate further.

For some time he loitered within the garden of the ramshackle cottage, occasionally leaping onto a windowsill in an attempt to take a peek through the layers of unwashed dirty glass and faded, yellowing net curtains that obscured his view. But his efforts to find out who lived in such a place were all to no avail because he simply could not see into the interior and two hours later he was still none the wiser as to who lived in the house.

By now he felt tired, hungry and thirsty and, to make matters worse, Ian was drenched to the skin for it was raining hard. All he wanted was somewhere to stay and his patience had long since worn thin but, at his wits end, he finally came up with an idea that would get the attention of the occupants of the house. Remembering how he had previously managed to disturb Mr Johnson, the neighbour who lived next door to his family home, Ian started to meow at the top of his voice, wailing and screeching in the most pitiful manner that he could muster up until a dim light eventually illuminated the glass window in the tatty old back door.

The owner of the house fumbled about with the door lock until, after what seemed like an age, it creaked open. Then a doddery old man poked his bearded face around the door frame, shining a torch with an equally feeble beam of light in all directions as he tried to pinpoint the painful sound that was seriously affecting his hearing. After studying the old man for a few moments Ian decided that he fitted the description Phillip had given him and believed that he had finally located the correct address known as Pussywillow House, therefore the sorrowful-looking cat stepped out of the shadows so that the old man could see him.

The old man's eyesight was none too good, especially in the dark, and it took him a while to make out the bedraggled specimen that now slouched before him, but when he did spot him he greeted the cat like a long-lost friend.

"Oh there you are," he said in a frail voice. "I could hear the hideous racket you were making but I couldn't see you in the dark with this awful weather. What a filthy night! Are you lost me old son? Why don't you come inside and sit by the fire, it'll be nice and warm in there and you'll soon dry off."

Ian took no prompting at all and he shot through the doorway faster than a rocket, almost knocking the old man off his feet as he did so. Once he was inside the cottage he shook his body violently, spraying moulting fur and dirty droplets of rainwater all over the walls of the short passageway that led to the kitchen. It took the old man a while to catch up with Ian after locking the back door and slowly hobbling along the corridor but he seemed to know exactly what the cat wanted and he quickly poured out a saucer of milk for the parched animal.

"There you go," he mumbled through his dense blue-grey whiskers, pushing the saucer in front of Ian's nose. "That should make you feel better."

Ian lapped up the milk with gusto while the old man disappeared into his pantry to produce a tin of mackerel fillets steeped in olive oil. His frail, shaky hands slowly peeled back the lid of the tin and he placed the entire contents into a scuffed plastic bowl that looked as if it had once belonged to another cat.

"I'm sure Dusty won't mind if you make use of her old bowl – She's long gone now anyway," said the old man. "Don't know why I kept it really… Memories, I suppose. It's just like everything else you keep: you hang on to these things believing that one day you'll make use of them, but it's rare that you do."

He placed the bowl of fish on the floor at Ian's feet and picked up the empty milk saucer, his old bones creaking as he struggled to bend down.

"My, you were thirsty weren't you?" exclaimed the old man. "I'll see if I can find a drop more milk for you just to keep you going through the night."

He went to the fridge again and poured the remainder of the milk from the bottle into the saucer.

"There goes my nightcap", sighed the old man, although he smiled at the same time. "Never mind, it's all in a good cause because I expect your needs are greater than mine after being caught out in such bad weather. Anyway, the milkman will be here early in the morning so we won't have to wait too long for our next supply to arrive."

The greedy cat didn't feel in the least bit guilty about depriving the old man of his nightcap and he gulped it down noisily, trying to drown out the sound of his lonely ramblings. Every once in a while Ian paused to draw breath and glance at the elderly fellow who burbled away constantly as he intently watched over the cat, almost as if he was purposely observing every movement he made. Even though he had never seen the bearded man before Ian couldn't help but think that there seemed to be something familiar about the old man's voice although he couldn't figure out exactly what it was. However, this was only a passing thought and he quickly blanked it out as he demolished the second saucer of milk.

Once Ian had finished his supper he began to take a vague interest in his surroundings for he had been so busy filling his face that he hadn't paid any attention before now. And what he saw dismayed him greatly. The kitchen he had been dining in was small and poky with cupboards so outdated they looked as if they had come straight out of Noah's Ark! He noticed that the room smelled rather damp and musty too, which was probably the reason why the linoleum floor covering was peeling away and parting company from the concrete surface beneath. It was blatantly obvious to Ian that the old man was very hard-up for cash and Ian was not going to be living in the lap of luxury like Phillip was; nonetheless, he at least had a roof over his head now and considered this to be marginally better than what he previously had. Feeling rather depressed by what he had seen of his surroundings so far Ian decided to wander off and check out the remainder of the cottage although he already knew it was going to get no better.

The old man had recently retired to his living room where he was napping in his favourite armchair that had seen much better days. He momentarily glanced up when the tortoiseshell cat nuzzled its head through the gap between the door and its frame before pushing his way into the dingy room and then he closed his eyes again before continuing to doze.

"Huh! This is going to be a no-frills experience and a real bundle of fun," Ian grumbled in disgust as he threw his body down onto a hearth rug in front of the fire. At that same moment the damp firewood crackled as it spat out a small fragment of burning embers to scorch yet another dark scar into the pile of the beige material. Ian thus decided to move safely out of harm's way of the fire to where the rug bordered a threadbare, flowery-patterned carpet tarnished by age. Once there, he made himself comfortable by tucking his paws beneath his body and then positioning his head so that his chin was touching the warm carpet before he settled down to sleep. After only a short while though he was awakened when the old man disturbed him.

"Here," he said. "I've looked out Dusty's old cat basket for you. It's brand new because she never did make use of it; and the bedding is new as well. It's lucky for you that I hung on to it all these years isn't it? Anyway, I'm off to bed now, goodnight me old son."

With that the old man erected a fireguard in front of the dying embers, turned off the light switch and left the room. Some loose treads creaked underfoot as he painfully climbed the stairs and then there was a series of bumps and thuds, the faint sound of squeaky bedsprings and finally silence apart from a steady tick-tock sound that came from a cuckoo clock shaped like a Swiss chalet that hung on the wall of the living room. To begin with, the noisy wooden bird frequently disturbed Ian's sleep pattern when every hour on the hour it protruded from within the confines of the clock to emit a loud, shrill cuckoo call when it proudly announced its precise method of timekeeping; however, the cat soon became accustomed to its

82

presence, enabling the sleepy animal to block the sound from its mind. When Ian next stirred he heard the cuckoo screech five times in quick succession and was then greeted by the frail but chirpy voice of the old man.

"Morning!" he said. "Did you sleep well?"

"Morning?" meowed the puzzled cat. "It's five o'clock, that's the middle of the flamin' night to me you silly old fool!"

"The milkman will be here at six o'clock," the old man told him as he clumsily tugged at the living room curtains, "then we can have a drink. I always like a cup of tea first thing, you know… I expect you'll be dying to go to the lavatory by now, so I'll leave the back door open and then you can come and go as you please."

The old man began to head towards the kitchen on his way to open the back door but then he paused for a moment, turned around and waggled his finger in the air as if he had just thought of something truly amazing.

"How presumptuous of me!" he exclaimed. "Perhaps you don't want to stay here at all. I mean, I've never seen you around here before and maybe you just needed somewhere to stay for the night away from that awful storm. Oh well, so be it, whatever you do is up to you. Anyway, it was nice to have a companion for a while even though I wasn't really very good company last night. I have good days and bad days you see young 'un, and yesterday was a bad one. I feel in my aching bones that today is going to be much better though. Now, what was I going to do? Oh yes, now I remember, I was going to open the back door wasn't I?"

Having jogged his memory the old man about-faced and resumed his path towards the kitchen, continuing to talk to the cat as he went because Ian was now right behind him.

"Come on, get a move on you stupid old twit," Ian meowed impatiently. "Open the flamin' door, I'm bustin' for a wee!"

As soon as the old man had opened the back door Ian rushed past him and fled out into the garden to carry out his much-needed ablutions. Afterwards he mooched idly around the garden, stretching his limbs and investigating his new territory. Then, at six o'clock, the milkman arrived on his early morning round, so Ian meandered back across the lawn eager for a saucer of milk.

"Morning Jim," Ian heard the old man say as he approached the front door of the cottage.

"Hello Ivan," greeted the milkman, a thick-set man with a shiny bald head and a large red nose. He nodded his head in Ian's direction and added: "I see you've got a new friend."

"Yes, he turned up in last night's storm. I thought he might have headed home by now though. Have you seen him around the neighbourhood before?"

"No, can't say that I have. Perhaps he's a stray. Mind you, I notice that he's got a collar and tag around his neck and it's unusual for a stray to have such a thing. Maybe it will have his address on it."

Jim bent down towards the ground and took a hold of Ian's collar with his left hand in order to study the name tag.

"Nope! There's no address on here, but it says that the cat's name is 'Ian'. That's a daft name for a cat isn't it?"

"In all my years I've never known an animal to be given such a plain and simple name," agreed Ivan, "but I think that our little friend here has been given an ordinary name which he more than makes up for with a very special personality."

"He doesn't look particularly special to me," replied Jim with a doubtful frown on his face. "Just a common moggy, and not a very pretty one at that. In fact, I'd go so far as to say that he's plain ugly if you ask me."

Even though Jim didn't mean any harm by what he said Ian took an instant dislike to him upon hearing this comment. Looking for an opportunity to get his own back Ian began to fuss around the milkman's legs and as soon as Jim stooped down to stroke the cat Ian immediately took a swipe at him, scratching the man's wrist and drawing a small amount of blood.

"Vicious little blighter as well," remarked Jim as he quickly drew his hand away.

"Yes, I guess he has got a bit of nasty streak in him," agreed Ivan. "But then again all cats do, it's in their nature."

"Yeah, next time I see you I'll scratch your face as well," Ian meowed angrily, still feeling insulted at being referred to as ugly.

"Oh well, there's no real harm done," said Jim after inspecting the minor damage to his wrist. "I'd love to stop and chat with you Ivan but I've got to be on my way or else the round will never get done. Same again tomorrow is it, just the one pint?"

"Better make it two, in case Ian the cat sticks around," replied the old man.

"Okay, I've made a mental note of that. Take care of yourself Ivan. Bye for now."

Ivan raised his hand in a gesture of farewell as his friend the milkman departed, and then he went indoors clutching the fresh pint of milk tightly in both hands as if it was a bottle of valuable gold dust. His next priority was to flick the switch on his kettle and whilst it was boiling the old fellow began to pour some milk into a saucer.

"Hoo-flippin-ray!" Ian meowed loudly as he thirstily watched the old man. "It's about time too."

"Oh, now that I've got some milk, all of a sudden you're talking to me are you?" chuckled the old man.

"No, I'm complaining actually," moaned Ian. "If only you understood what I was really saying. Come on, hurry up you old fool, I'm starving."

The ungrateful cat wolfed down his liquid breakfast in no time at all and then looked longingly at the old man for a second helping.

"What, you want more?" said Ivan. "I reckon you should have been named Oliver instead of Ian! At this rate you'll be eating me out of house and home. No matter, I'll have a word with my home help later on and see if he'll fetch some dried meal and tinned food from the local store if you're going to be staying here for a while. How does that sound?"

"Whoopee-do!" meowed Ian sarcastically. "I can't wait to try it."

Well, Ian did indeed get to taste some cat food later that day because Ivan's home help turned up and delivered several sealed packets in an assortment of flavours. Ian didn't get to meet the home help though because he was taking a catnap at the time of his visit and when he awoke the man had already gone.

Half asleep, Ian wandered into the kitchen and after noticing the hungry expression on the cat's face Ivan placed the opened sample packets on the floor in front of him whereupon Ian was then forced to try them all in order to determine his favourite flavour. To begin with, the fussy cat turned up his nose in disgust as he looked at the offerings. 'Fit for human consumption', stated the printed words on the packets, so Ian thought that it must therefore be okay for cats to eat as well and he reluctantly decided to taste it. The pungent odour of the meat was extremely off-putting at first but once he had got over this initial hurdle it tasted quite edible and to his surprise he actually liked it.

Chicken with funny-coloured bits of stuff in it turned out to be his favourite flavour because the taste reminded him of a casserole his mother used to make. He had always turned up his nose in disgust when she had served that dish for his evening meal because it tasted awful to him, but at the present time this distant memory was enough to make him savour the moment, and he thought how strange it was that his life's current twists and turns had made him appreciate the simple things a little more.

The well-fed animal quickly settled into his new life at old Ivan's abode and it didn't take him long to discover that if he wanted something all he had to do was leap onto the old man's lap and meow profusely. The only disadvantage of this was that Ivan always petted and stroked him, talking to him as if he was a big baby. How

Ian hated that. And then, worse still, there was the hugging and kissing thing – Yuk! Regardless of this, he let the old man get away with it for short periods of time and when he'd had enough of being fussed to death Ian easily managed to wriggle free of his clutches. As far as Ian was concerned this home was only a temporary stop-gap until he could move on to better things, but in the meantime he was heeding Adolf the dog's advice when he had been told not to bite the hand that fed him. He knew that he would have to grin and bear this new lifestyle for the time being because it was in his own interests so that he would be well cared for and it would only be a short-term affair.

Besides, if Ian really wanted to escape from the old man he could find plenty of places to hide where he wouldn't be disturbed. There was the broken air-brick in the kitchen wall for instance: here was a great place where he could lose himself because it led to several cavities beneath the floorboards. And this was the very spot where Ian discovered Ivan's horde of money. It seemed that the old man didn't possess a bank account and throughout his apparently poverty-stricken lifetime he had scrimped and saved every spare penny that he could, stashing it away underneath the floorboards of his living room ready for a rainy day. But it was obvious to Ian that the rainy day had never come because Ivan hadn't splashed out on any rich trappings that could have so improved his meagre existence.

There was a small fortune tucked away beneath the floorboards, neatly bundled away in wads of notes wrapped together with a damp-resistant polythene covering, and now that Ian knew of its whereabouts greed came the better of him. The cunning cat thought that when he eventually reverted back to his human form he would plan a return visit to Ivan's home and rob the old man blind of his life's savings. After all, why waste it he thought? What good was the money to the old codger? He had no children or family to leave it to and he wasn't going to spend it on himself, so it would make more sense for Ian to make better use of it.

All Ian had to do now was to keep his nose clean and stay out of trouble in order to survive his Sentence of Nine Lives with at least one life left intact and then The Catmaster would transform him back into his human form. After that he could easily steal Ivan's money, go on a massive spending spree and have so much fun.

However, staying out of trouble was going to prove to be easier said than done because trouble was Ian's middle name and it was something that he found difficult to avoid.

CHAPTER EIGHT

The Runaway Cat

There was really nothing much for Ian to do in his new world except eat, sleep or lounge around, and the tortoiseshell cat was quickly becoming bored with his lot. After one particularly lazy day, just as dusk was approaching, Ian pestered Ivan to be allowed outside because it was getting near to the time of day that cats liked best of all… nightfall.

Cats are nocturnal creatures by habit, and so long as the weather remains dry the hours of darkness become their adventure playground. The streets come alive after dark as a variety of nocturnal creatures go about their business with their fabulous natural gift of night vision and the feline species is no exception to this rule. Every night cats spill out of the comfort of their homes to jockey for position as rulers of their domain for they are very territorial creatures with each one possessing their own little patch and, as yet, Ian had not been seen in his neighbourhood so he thought that it was about time he made himself known.

Immediately after he had stepped out into the rear garden of Ivan's home Ian raised his head and sniffed the air. His in-built barometer told him there was no sign of rain present in the atmosphere and, content with this, he casually mooched around the lawn and flowerbeds for a while before venturing through the garden gate that led to the paved streets beyond.

After he had squeezed between the wrought iron bars of the gate he suddenly became aware of a nearby presence. Turning quickly around in the street he noticed a pair of identical-looking cats sitting very still on either side of the garden gate like ornaments made of china, holding their bodies majestically upright and having an aloof air of superiority about their manner. Believing that he could play the same game as them Ian planted his backside firmly on the ground, raised his head, narrowed his eyes and looked down his nose at the other cats.

"What are you staring at?" he grunted.

"You!" said the Siamese cats in a sing-song harmony, unmoved by Ian's hostile attitude towards them.

"Well, mind your own business and get lost," warned Ian, "this is my territory."

"Charming!" replied the Siamese cats together. "If we'd known you were going to talk to us like that we wouldn't have bothered coming to welcome you to the neighbourhood."

"To be honest, I couldn't care less whether you had come or not."

"Fine! Be like that if you must. We were told to come and greet you by The Catmaster who led us to believe that you were a very pleasant fellow Phillip."

91

"Wait a minute… *Phillip?* Did you call me Phillip?"

"Yes, we did," the reply came back in stereo. "That's your name isn't it?"

"No, I'm Ian. Can't you read?" he mocked, deliberately flicking his name tag with one of his paws.

"Then there must be some mistake", said the two disappointed Siamese.

"No, there hasn't been a mistake. Phillip won't be coming after all; I've taken his place you see. Like it or lump it, I'm your new neighbour."

"So, you're an imposter huh? We shall have to tell this news to The Catmaster and see what he has to say about the matter. We're sure he won't like it one little bit."

"We're sure he won't like it one little bit," sneered Ian trying to imitate their voices. "If you dare tell The Catmaster that I'm here then you'll both regret saying it."

"Is that a threat?" chimed the pair of Siamese cats.

"No, it's a promise," warned Ian.

At that moment the Siamese cats stood up to leave.

"Where are you going?" Ian demanded to know.

"We're going to tell Harlequin about you."

"Oh no you're not," yelled Ian taking on an aggressive stance, and in the next instant he launched himself towards the identical cats.

All of a sudden World War Three broke out in Coalpit Road. Fur, fangs and claws flew in all directions as the three cats became engrossed in a furious battle and for the following few moments the sound of angry wailing filled the air, mixed together with occasional

92

howls of pain. Although they put up an equally vicious fight the wiry Siamese cats did not have the power to match their tortoiseshell counterpart and Ian eventually emerged as the conquering victor. When the catfight was finally over he stood back and surveyed the aftermath.

One of the Siamese had managed to tear itself away from the affray where it now hid in a hedgerow fighting for breath, whilst the other cat lay motionless upon the ground. Ian was horrified. He had wanted to bully the cats into submission but he hadn't intended to inflict such harsh wounds upon them. Now that he was sure to face the wrath of The Catmaster for his latest crimes he felt there was no option left open to him but to run away, so he dragged his bruised and battered form painfully along the pavement and cowardly melted into the night.

As luck would have it Ian soon stumbled across a delivery truck parked at the roadside with its rear doors open. The moon was full and in the pallid blue glow of twilight he could see that the colour of its livery was maroon and cream and beautifully sign-written upon the vehicle's coach-built bodywork were the words:

OVERNIGHT EXPRESS
RETURN TRIPS FROM ENGLAND TO SCOTLAND

Ian had never been to Scotland and it seemed like a faraway place to visit, therefore he stealthily leapt through the open doors of the wagon where he hid himself from view amongst its cargo. A short while later the rear doors were slammed shut before the truck trundled away on its long-distance trip and Ian began to while away the time by licking clean the many wounds that he had sustained during his recent fight. All of a sudden a hazy blue light filled the interior of the truck forcing Ian to stop what he was doing and look up and then, without warning, another cat materialized out of thin air startling the living daylights out of him.

"Hello Stinky," said the beautiful, mysterious Birman that he had first encountered when he had been expelled from Catland a couple of days earlier.

"Uh? How did you get in here?" asked Ian in utter astonishment.

"You'd be surprised where I can go," she replied.

"Are you following me or something?"

"Perhaps… Are you going somewhere nice?"

"Yes, I'm going to Scotland actually. I've never been there before."

"It's no good running away, you know, The Catmaster will always find you, wherever you are."

"If I need your advice I'll ask for it," retorted Ian arrogantly, yet his voice was somewhat shaky because he felt a little worried at the thought of The Catmaster coming after him.

"Why do you feel the need to fight the World?" asked the mysterious cat in a soft voice and ignoring his aggressive attitude towards her. "I'm only here to help you, you know."

"I don't need any help."

"Oh, but I think you do Stinky."

"Look! Stop calling me Stinky."

"I'll stop calling you Stinky only when you lose your attitude."

"Just leave me alone will ya. In other words, GO AWAY!"

"You're not at all big on conversation are you? That's twice now that you've told me to go away – we'll never get to know each other at this rate. Very well then, I will go away, but not until I have said what I came here to say…"

"And that is?" Ian interrupted.

"That is: if you ever need me – and I'm sure you will – just call my name out loud."

"I don't even know your name," sneered Ian.

"My name is Sorcha (that's spelt S-O-R-C-H-A by the way but pronounced SORSHA as if it has a letter 's' instead of a 'c')."

"Who cares how you spell your name? Okay, so now you've said what you wanted to say… Goodbye and good riddance!"

Sorcha smiled at him sweetly. "Goodbye for now Stinky," she said. "Oh, by the way, the Siamese cat you beat up is going to be alright. She was simply knocked unconscious for a few seconds so there was no need for you to have run away after all."

Having informed Ian of this good news Sorcha then vanished as quickly as she had appeared. Ian breathed a sigh of relief safe in the knowledge that he hadn't killed the Siamese cat during the fight after all, and with his mind put at rest he curled up and fell asleep. He was disturbed several times during the long, tedious journey up north though because each time the delivery truck hit a pothole in the road he was flung all over the place, but eventually the truck came to a gentle halt when it reached its destination. By this time the runaway tortoiseshell was starving, thirsty and desperate to go to the lavatory, so as soon as the rear doors were opened up he made a dash for freedom and escaped unnoticed by the sleepy truck driver.

Ian took a good look at his surroundings now that he was in the big outdoors, and it really did seem big too. Everywhere he looked there was nothing to be seen but miles and miles of mountainous countryside covered with pine trees that towered high above him. The ruggedness of the terrain seemed quite frightening to Ian because he had never set foot in such a remote area before but, regardless of this, he hadn't come all this way for nothing and so he set off to explore. He walked for several miles up and down hill through dense pine forests until he found his way barred by a wide river that cut a deep gorge through the mountainside. Ian was not impressed by this at all having walked for so long but there was no choice other than to turn around and head away in another direction.

It came to his attention that the air quality was much more crisp and clear in the high peaks of the mountains than it was back home and now that night had fallen the temperature was far lower too. My, but how cold it had suddenly become, so much so that the cool air was causing his eyes to water and run and this moisture was forming a thin frozen veil which made his vision become blurred. Every now and again the disorientated cat had to stop to rub his weeping eyes and wipe his dripping nose and he was deeply regretting having left the warmth of his new home far behind. In fact, his eyesight was becoming so bad that he was beginning to hallucinate... or so he thought.

On one occasion he stopped to clear his eyes because he believed he had seen a giant cat on the trail ahead of him but when he rubbed them and removed his paws the large cat was still there, so it wasn't a figment of his imagination after all. The animal was at least twice the size of him with a dirty tabby type of coat and it glared menacingly at him through wild-looking eyes before crouching down low to the ground, wriggling its rear end like cats do when they are preparing to pounce on their prey.

"This is all I need," groaned Ian in despair. "I'm not afraid of you, ya big pussy! If it's a fight you want, then I'll give you one."

The fierce-looking cat didn't reply in Ian's cat language but instead an eerie squawking sound was emitted from its throat that echoed throughout the forest, causing the hairs on Ian's neck and back to rise and sending tingling shivers racing along his spine. In the next instance the wild cat sprang forward and at that very moment Ian was suddenly overcome by a strange sensation which engulfed his entire body and sent him hurtling across the forest floor in the opposite direction, his feet barely touching the ground.

"Wha... what's happening to me?" he asked out loud in a strange-sounding, wobbly voice that no longer seemed to belong to him. "I don't understand – I never run away from a fight."

"On this occasion you must! Be quiet and keep those limbs moving," ordered an equally wobbly and yet slightly familiar voice that came from somewhere within his body.

"*YOU!*" Ian shouted abruptly. "But how... What? Get out of me!"

"I said shut-up, and stop working against me will you?"

Ian had no choice but to do as he was told because although he tried as hard as possible he couldn't shake off the Birman cat that had somehow entered his body and taken over control of his limbs.

97

After quite some time the runaway cat left the forest far behind and found himself back on a tarmac road surface where his paws finally ceased to run any more. He was then forcefully flopped down onto his backside whilst the female cat attempted to leave his body.

"What are you doing now?" groaned Ian impatiently.

"I'm trying to get out," replied Sorcha. "For goodness sake, keep still and stop trying to fight against me again."

"I can't help it; it's a natural defence mechanism of mine."

"Well, think of something else to take your mind off it."

"Like what?"

"I don't know, something nice like… like Christmas, for instance."

Ian accepted this decoy willingly as his thoughts momentarily turned to Christmas time and all the nice things that came with it, thus enabling Sorcha's spirit to break free of him. Then, having allowed himself time to regain his breath and composure, the bewildered tortoiseshell eventually managed to find his voice again.

"That was really weird. How did you manage to do that Sorcha?"

"Oh, you've remembered my name now have you? That's much more civil of you."

"Cut the sarcasm, I asked you a question," Ian replied in a surly manner.

"There's no need to be so rude, especially now that I have just saved your life."

"Saved my life? What are you talking about?"

"From that Scottish wild cat… It would have ripped you to shreds."

"So that's what that big brute was, a Scottish wild cat. I wasn't afraid of it you know, I could have taken it on and won."

"Yeah, right! In your dreams maybe."

"I told the monster that I'd give it a fight and I was ready for him," boasted Ian.

"It was a 'her' actually, and she doesn't talk in the language of domestic cats. She was going to kill you and then eat you all up. I don't expect any thanks from you but it was fortunate for you that I was around at the time."

Ian shrugged his shoulders. "Bully for you... So what?"

"You will still lose one of your nine lives automatically though," Sorcha warned him, "because, in reality, you would have lost your real life."

At the very moment that Sorcha had finished saying this sentence there was a 'PHUT-PHUT, FIZZ!' sound and an amber crystal on Ian's collar instantly turned black. He glanced nonchalantly at it and shrugged his shoulders again as if he didn't care.

"Anyway," he said, "You still haven't answered my question... How did you manage to get inside my body and take control of my movements? Are you a ghost or something like that?"

"Not exactly," sighed Sorcha in a noticeably sad tone of voice.

"Then what, exactly, are you?"

"I'm a Permanent Cat – a guardian angel in other words."

At first Ian laughed disbelievingly but then this transformed into a nervous titter when he realized that she wasn't kidding.

"You're serious aren't you?" he gasped.

Sorcha nodded her head in agreement.

"But only humans have guardian angels, if you believe in that sort of thing," said Ian as he struggled to accept the fact that this information was true.

"Guardian angels really do exist, Stinky," Sorcha assured him rather snappily. "And not just for humans either, but for all living creatures."

Ian laughed again. "Even for ants?" he mocked.

"Yes, even for ants."

"They must be what are known as flying ants then," joked Ian.

Sorcha just went along with him and smiled in her usual sweet way.

"So, how did you become a guardian angel? I mean, what were you before that?" asked Ian.

"A cat, just like I appear now except that I'm what is known as a Permanent Cat these days."

"What does that mean?"

"Just as the word describes: I am here permanently... forever... always," explained Sorcha.

"I don't understand. If you were once a cat and now you're a cat again, what happened in between?"

"I died!"

"Oh!" gasped Ian in surprise because he wasn't expecting such a reply. "How?"

"I was killed by a boy on a skateboard."

Ian was flabbergasted because he wasn't expecting to hear that either. It took a few moments for the full truth of the matter to sink in before he managed to find a reply.

"So, you've come back to haunt me have you?" he sobbed. "I didn't mean to do it. It was an accident Sorcha, honestly it was."

"I know it was an accident," Sorcha bravely reassured him. "And no, I haven't come back to haunt you at all; I'm here to help you, like I explained to you earlier."

"But why do you want to help me after the terrible thing I've done to you?"

"I don't hold a grudge against you Stinky; it was my own stupid fault for being in that place at that particular time. I had already lost eight lives in the past through my own carelessness – you know, usual cat stuff like falling out of trees, getting knocked over by cars, etc – so I should have been more careful with the last precious life that I possessed. It's as simple as that. Anyway, what's done is done and I've been sent to watch over you. It's time that you started taking more care as well, because with three lives definitely gone (and there's sure to be more the next time you meet Harlequin) you're heading in the right direction to become a Permanent Cat too."

"So, what do you suggest that I do now?"

"Right now I suggest that you go home Ian."

"You called me Ian," he said in delight.

"I know. It was a slip of the tongue."

"Oh," exclaimed Ian showing obvious disappointment. "Never mind... So how do I get out of here? I have no idea where the truck is that I arrived in or where I am right now, apart from the fact that I'm in Scotland."

"The truck has long since gone," Sorcha informed him, "but there are always other ways of getting home."

"Such as?"

"Well, if you walk in a southerly direction – and because you are a cat your instinct will naturally tell you which way the south lies – you will find a railway station where you can catch a train and hopefully it will put your life back on track if you have not gone too far off the rails by that time."

"Ha-ha, very funny!" sneered Ian.

"Yes, very funny indeed. However, the funniest bit is yet to come because the railway station is at least two days' walk from here! Goodbye Stinky, have fun," sniggered Sorcha, and then she vanished into thin air.

CHAPTER NINE

The Ninth Life

A further two weeks passed before Ian returned home because the silly cat became hopelessly lost. The main reason for this was due to the gentle rocking of a train's carriages as it travelled along a railway track which sent Ian to sleep and this in turn always made him miss the station where he needed to get off. After missing several stops the adventurous cat gave up trying to get home and decided instead to see a bit more of the country in which he lived.

It was great fun to begin with because everything was new to him and as soon as he got fed up with a particular route then he would simply hop onto another train and go elsewhere. The wily youngster fussed around the passengers who were amazed to see a cat travelling on a train, which also served another purpose to Ian for it meant that they gave him scraps of food and he was therefore well fed. Of course the porters on board the trains vowed to hand the stray cat over to the station master at the next convenient stop but the crafty animal managed to elude them by finding somewhere to hide or hopping off and getting onto another train. Eventually though, having travelled the length and breadth of the country for nearly two weeks the whole experience became tedious and Ian finally chose to go home.

Upon his return to Ivan's cottage in Coalpit Road the roaming tortoiseshell was greeted by the two ginger tomcats known as Trojan and Spartan, but the two sentries were certainly not there to welcome him home. As usual Trojan did the talking and Spartan said nothing.

"The Catmaster wishes to speak with you immediately," Trojan told him.

"I'll see him tomorrow," replied Ian rather haughtily. "He'll have to wait – I'm too tired right now."

"I don't think you heard me correctly... I said IMMEDIATELY!" growled Trojan.

Ian could tell that Trojan was not in the mood for any nonsense and he thought that it was wise to give in or he would have to suffer the consequences.

"Alright, alright; keep your fur on!" he surrendered with the sulkiest scowl on his face.

"What's the big rush all about anyhow?"

"You'll find out when you get there. Come along now – get a move on."

Flanked on either side by the ginger sentries Ian was thus frog-marched to the foot of Sunrise Hill whereupon they halted outside the front entrance to Catland.

"I'm not allowed to use this entrance," said Ian with a smug expression on his face.

"On this occasion we don't have a choice," grumbled Trojan. "But we'll have to blindfold you."

"Huh? What on Earth for? I know exactly where we're going, you know – I've been here before."

"Nevertheless, we have to blindfold all non-members of Catland when they use the front entrance... It's traditional," Trojan continued.

"Great! Now I'm going to end up looking an ugly brute just like you," said Ian pointing at Trojan's eye patch.

"That's enough!" snapped the offended sentry nervously adjusting his eye patch. "You don't know when to give it a rest do you Kid? Now shut up or we'll gag you as well."

"You wouldn't dare!" Ian defiantly challenged him.

"Oh no?" said Trojan with a wicked glint in his eye. "Well, try this for size then."

Trojan hurriedly whipped the bandana from around Spartan's neck and wrapped it around Ian's face. This served a dual purpose because the bandana was large enough to blindfold the cheeky cat and gag him at the same time.

"That's better. Now we can all get some peace," grinned Trojan.

Ian was fuming but there was absolutely nothing he could do about it because Spartan held his paws firmly behind his back. Secured in this same position he was then forced roughly through the entrance to Catland where he was taken to face the wrath of Harlequin.

"Ah! The wanderer finally returns," said Harlequin. "Long time no see."

"Yeah, you're right, I can't see a flippin' thing," mumbled Ian. "Take this blindfold off me right this minute."

"That's not exactly what I meant; however, the blindfold and gag can now be removed please Spartan."

Spartan duly carried out his master's request and once the blindfold had been taken off Ian discovered that he was back in the courtroom at Catland again, but this time there was only Harlequin, Gubbins and the two ginger sentries present.

"Why have you brought me here?" demanded the angry tortoiseshell.

"Silence! You are in no position to ask questions until I have said my piece," growled Harlequin. "I am not very happy with you at present because I have had to call an emergency court hearing – you are in very serious trouble young fellow. There are some matters of great importance that need to be dealt with immediately... before it's too late."

"Too late for what?" asked Ian deliberately ignoring The Catmaster's request for silence.

Gubbins raised one of his bony paws to his lips. "Sssh!" he whispered calmly, "and you will find out. Listen very carefully to what has to be said."

"Thank-you Gubbins... Now Ian, if you can recall you were warned that if you were to lose all of your nine lives then you would remain in feline form forever. Well, it appears that you are perilously near to the occurrence of this event."

"But I've only lost three lives so far, so how can that be?" Ian boasted.

"That is where you are very wrong. It has been quite a while since we last saw you and during your period of absence you have caused a great deal of grief within the cat fraternity for which you are about to lose yet more of your lives."

Ian rolled his eyes and shook his head in a gesture of bored exasperation which didn't go unnoticed by Harlequin. In fact, this just made The Catmaster even angrier.

"How dare you look at me in such a way. We have been very patient up to now and everyone has tried to help you in whatever way possible, but now I am at the end of my tether with you and so without further ado I shall now admonish your punishment. To begin with you will instantly lose your fourth life for mixing up my spell books when you wrongfully entered Catland – It took Gubbins and I a long time to put them back in order!"

'PHUT-PHUT, FIZZ!' went the sound as Harlequin waved his furry paws in the air, and a fourth amber crystal on Ian's collar turned black. This didn't seem to bother Ian at all. Instead, he simply grinned as he remembered the results of this big mix-up and how poor Phillip had been turned into a female house cat, but still he didn't tell Harlequin about the hapless creature's whereabouts.

"Do you have anything to say about this matter?" asked Harlequin.

There followed a stony silence in the courtroom whilst Harlequin waited for an answer. The Catmaster peered into the depths of the tortoiseshell's eyes expecting a full confession on this matter for he secretly knew about Phillip's predicament, but an admission from the guilty juvenile was still not forthcoming. With a cocky grin stretched

107

right across his face Ian tried to outstare The Catmaster's penetrating gaze.

"Well?" said Harlequin at length. "I'm waiting for an answer. Do you have anything else to tell me?"

"No!" Ian deliberately replied.

"Very well, you've had your chance. You will now lose your fifth life for failing to tell me about Phillip and the great hardship you have caused him."

'PHUT-PHUT, FIZZ!'

"How… How did you know about what had happened to him?" asked Ian, whose smile had suddenly disappeared from his face as the shock of being found out overwhelmed him.

"We know everything that goes on," Gubbins chimed in. "You see, in our cat world folk stick together and watch out for each other rather than allow the selfish attitude that human's have adopted to rule our lives. We have learned a lot from *your* mistakes."

"Life number six," Harlequin continued, "is to be subtracted for the fight you had with the two Siamese cats."

"Huh! It was just a fight. Everyone has a fight at some time or another."

"That is a fact, I agree; however, the Siamese cats were merely girls! It is not the done thing for boys to fight with girls at all."

"Uh? Oh! How was I supposed to know they were girls?"

"Surely a boy of your age should be aware of the difference by now."

"Of course I know the difference," Ian replied scornfully.

"Therefore you should know better. Nevertheless, you have still lost another life."

"PHUT-PHUT, FIZZ!"

"And then there is the serious crime of attempting to steal my... I mean... the old man's life savings."

"What are you talking about? I didn't steal any of his money."

"No, but you were thinking about doing so at some time in the future."

"How can you possibly be able to read my mind?"

"Cats have extra senses," Gubbins interrupted.

"Like I've already said, I didn't steal it," protested Ian. "I was only moving it to a safer place."

"We are quite aware of your intentions, so I'm not going to argue with you – Lose another life," Harlequin insisted.

'PHUT-PHUT, FIZZ!'

"...That's number seven by the way."

"I'm not stupid, I can count you know!" Ian retorted.

"In that case you will be aware that the eighth life comes next and this one will be deducted for purposely running away from home and not facing up to your problems."

'PHUT-PHUT, FIZZ!'

"Finally, number nine: for failing to turn up for your appointment with me..."

"I was lost," was Ian's feeble excuse.

"Lost? Yeah, really! You were having the time of your life travelling up and down the country by train."

"M'Lord?" Gubbins said questioningly as he interrupted again in an attempt to get Harlequin's attention.

But The Catmaster didn't hear his assistant because he was so engrossed in what he was doing, and this was going to be a bit of a problem because Gubbins had realized that The Catmaster was about to take away Ian's final life. At exactly the same moment Ian had also realized what was happening and he had suddenly become aware of the consequences of losing his ninth life.

"NO!" yelled Ian at the top of his voice. "You can't take away my ninth life because I'll stay as a cat forever and I don't want to be one."

"It's too late," Harlequin sneered, "You should have been more careful."

"HARLEQUIN!" screamed Gubbins at the top of his voice.

"What? What is it Gubbins?"

"Can I have a quiet word in your ear please?"

"What, now? Can't you see that I'm busy?"

"Yes M'Lord, but I need to speak with you NOW."

"Is it important?"

"Extremely!"

"Oh, very well then, but make it quick because I have some unfinished business to attend to."

Gubbins hurriedly approached Harlequin and proceeded to whisper into The Catmaster's ear.

"I think you're overlooking the fact that if you take away Ian's ninth life then he will become a Permanent Cat," he informed Harlequin.

110

"Not at all," replied Harlequin. "I was just having a little joke with the youngster. I knew you would interrupt me before I had administered the full punishment."

"Phew! You certainly had me fooled for a moment or two. I thought you were serious... And so did Ian. Just look at him blubbering away over there."

Harlequin looked at Ian and then he began to snigger.

"Did I have you fooled as well Gubbins? Oh, how marvellous."

"It wasn't that funny Harlequin."

"Well, it appealed to my sense of humour at least. Come now Gubs, I was only trying to make the lad think about his situation in order to frighten him into changing his ways and, by golly, I believe my ploy is going to work."

"Hmm? Normally I trust your judgement but in this case I really don't have too much faith," said Gubbins rather doubtfully.

"Well, the moment of truth has arrived, my dear fellow. It's now or never I believe; let's conclude this hearing and see what happens."

Gubbins quietly returned to his stone pew while Harlequin resumed his conversation with Ian.

"Eight lives have now been lost young man, and I was about to take away your ninth..."

"Please don't take my life away," Ian pleaded with tears rolling down his cheeks. "I promise to become a better person – or cat – from now on."

"Okay, just this once I shall be more than fair to you and include that last offence in the eighth life category. You will have one last chance to make amends. Presently there are eight black crystals on your collar and only one now glows with the fire of life, so you have a reprieve."

"Oh, thank-you so much," gasped Ian.

"Consider yourself very fortunate because not everyone gets a second chance at life. Well, there is nothing more that remains to be said; you must leave now and this time I really do expect a happy ending," said Harlequin in a stern voice. "Good-bye Ian. Leave by the back door there's a good chap. Trojan and Spartan will accompany you out of Catland."

CHAPTER TEN

Saved By a Whisker

Not for the first time, but hopefully for the last, the rejected tortoiseshell was escorted from the courtroom by the two ginger sentries who had stood silently throughout this second trial. For once in his life Ian did not have anything at all to say to the guards as he was evicted forcibly from Catland to inevitably slide down the slippery tunnel and end up face down in the stinking slurry pit at the foot of Sunrise Hill.

Feeling very down in the dumps, Ian licked the disgusting, foul-smelling cow pooh from his fur whilst he pondered what to do next. Then he remembered his guardian angel, the Permanent Cat.

"Sorcha, where are you?" he asked out loud. "I need you Sorcha, please help me... SORCHA!"

"Well, well, well – this really is a turn up for the books. Not only did you ask for me by name, but you said 'please' as well!" came the welcoming sound of a friendly voice.

Ian raised his head slowly. It felt as if there was a heavy black cloud hanging above him and everything was now such an effort. He glanced at the elegant Birman cat that was perched on the overhanging sewer pipe, her glowing hazy aura seemingly brighter than ever before that made her beauty appear even more enchanting. Then he lowered his head again without a single word being uttered from between his sorrowful-looking lips.

"What's the matter Stinky? Cat got your tongue?" asked Sorcha trying to provoke a reaction.

But there was no fancy retort or any sarcastic comment as would usually be expected from the cheeky, mischievous tortoiseshell. In fact, the fire of fury that had burned within Ian's heart for so long had disappeared to be replaced with a stone-cold numbness that he had never previously felt. The ordeal that he had just been through in Catland with him having come so close to losing his ninth life had finally had the desired effect and sunk in to his tiny brain. Ian was now a very frightened, worried cat. Realizing the sensitivity of the situation caused by these new emotions that Ian was experiencing Sorcha nimbly leapt from the sewer pipe and nuzzled close by Ian's side.

"Don't be afraid," she whispered soothingly. "I will help you through your troubled times."

"I have never asked anyone for anything during my entire life Sorcha, but I really do need your help right now because I don't know what to do."

"Sometimes everyone needs to ask for help. There's nothing wrong with that Ian, it's perfectly normal and quite acceptable."

"Not for me it isn't."

"Yes, even for you it is."

"So, where do I go from here? I mean, what shall I do next?"

"Well, for a start you could turn over a new leaf and make a fresh start in life."

"But where do I begin?"

"At the very beginning of course, by correcting some of the wrong-doings you have caused recently."

"There were so many of them," Ian confessed.

"Yes, I know, but now's your chance to make amends and regain some of your lost lives."

"But surely it's too late," said Ian in a despondent voice.

"It's never too late to make amends Ian. Why not start by paying a visit to the old man in Coalpit Road?"

"You mean Ivan?"

"Yes, Ivan – I'm sure he will be delighted to see you – and then take things as they come and see what a difference you can make."

"Are you coming with me Sorcha?"

"No, I can only advise you on what you need to do; the rest is up to you. You can do it Ian, I know you can… I truly believe in you."

"You do? Well, you're the first person (or cat for that matter) that ever has believed in me. Thanks Sorcha, what you have just said means a lot to me."

Immediately Ian seemed to perk up, as if a great burden had suddenly been lifted from his shoulders. Sorcha could tell by the sparkle that had returned to his eyes that he was feeling better.

"It's good to talk and share your problems isn't it?" said Sorcha with a beaming smile upon her face.

"I had never realized before, but yes, I agree with you, it is good to talk…and I've noticed that you're calling me Ian again."

"Well, I think it's a much nicer name than Stinky and you deserve to have your old name back now that you are reforming."

"Thanks! And thanks for coming to help me Sorcha."

Ian stepped forward, threw his furry limbs around the Permanent Cat and gave her the biggest hug of her life.

"Steady on Ian, I'm quite fragile you know," said Sorcha, feeling slightly embarrassed by Ian's surprise embrace. "Anyway, I'm glad to have been able to help you. Oh, by the way, do you remember that cosy rug I gave you some time ago? Well, I rescued it from the river just after you had thrown it away and I stored it away in the coal bunker at Pussywillow House: you *really* may need it one of these days."

"Thanks again," said Ian rather sheepishly, then he stood up and stretched his limbs. "I've got to go now Sorcha, see you soon. I will be seeing you again won't I?"

"Undoubtedly", Sorcha reassured him. "Good luck Ian."

Having said that the Permanent Cat vanished into thin air and Ian set off along the banks of the river.

After walking in the direction of the river flow for about half-a-mile Ian rounded a bend and there, sitting in the middle of the narrow track and blocking his path, was Trojan. It was unusual to see him alone for the ginger tom was apparently inseparable from his friend Spartan, but for some reason or another he was on his own as if he was purposely waiting for Ian to pass that way.

Stealthily Ian sidled around Trojan eyeing the sentry warily whilst Trojan watched him with his one good eye. Neither cat uttered a single word; that is until Ian was safely past his arch-enemy. Then, curiosity got the better of him and Ian felt the need to say something.

"Why do you hate me Trojan?"

"It's not personal Kid, I dislike most children."

"I'm not a child, I'm a cat!"

"Yeah, but you're only a pretend one aren't you."

Ian was offended by this remark and Trojan's attempt at needling him obviously worked because he quickly rose to the bait.

"You think you're so tough don't you? What, with your pathetic looking eye patch to try and make you seem hard. Well, you don't scare me one little bit."

"That's not the reason why I wear it at all. The patch actually serves a purpose."

"So why do you wear the patch Trojan? You look ridiculous."

"If I need your opinion Kid I'll ask for it."

While the two cats were in discussion Ian had been moving around cautiously and he was now standing to the side of Trojan without the eye patch when he realized that the ginger tom was staring directly in front of him as he spoke to the fired-up tortoiseshell. It suddenly dawned on him that Trojan couldn't see very well out of his good eye either so he said nothing else but crept further around the sentry instead, waving his paws in the air as he did so. Sure enough, Trojan couldn't see him, and a wicked idea began to form in Ian's head which he rapidly put to use.

"I'm over here," yelled Ian.

"What?" said Trojan quickly turning his head to face the tortoiseshell.

But Ian had already moved.

"Now I'm over here, shouted the tortoiseshell."

Trojan swivelled his head once more in the opposite direction just as Ian flitted back again. Then, without warning, he charged at the ginger tom and crashed into him with all his might.

"Look at me now Trojan," Ian declared triumphantly, at the same time tearing at the eye patch. "I've filled out a bit and I told you I'd get even with you one day."

Ian was right. He had gained some weight since his early days as a cat and his extra body weight, combined with the speed in which he had rushed into Trojan, caused the larger animal to be knocked off-balance. With Trojan caught entirely off-guard this allowed the angry youngster to successfully wrench the eye patch from the other cat's head, and then he stepped backwards to take a good look at his unmasked opponent. But the smirk on Ian's face quickly turned to a look of horror because the eye patch really did serve a purpose just as Trojan had told him. Beneath it were the ugly wounds that Trojan had sustained as a result of a firework prank carried out by a group of juveniles two years previous in which he had lost an eye. All that remained where the eye had once been was a sewn-up slit and a mass of scar tissue caused by scorching gunpowder from the firework as it had gouged into the surrounding skin.

By now Trojan had scrambled to his feet where he recoiled in embarrassment as he tried to cover up the horrific wounds that he had kept hidden for so long. In doing so he took several steps backwards before losing his footing on the moss-covered rocks at the river's edge and plunged into its muddy waters. Meanwhile, Ian remained rooted to the spot, still reeling from the shock of what he had done and seen. Suddenly the sound of Spartan's voice as he raced along the riverbank made Ian snap out of his nightmarish trance.

"Quick, do something, cats can't swim... My brother can't swim!" Spartan yelled in panic.

Without any further hesitation Ian dived into the river to rescue Trojan for although he had been turned into a cat he still retained his human capability of being able to swim. He paddled furiously, swimming with the strong current until he reached the stricken animal whose lifeless form sank beneath the surface just before Ian got to him. Following him down, Ian searched the murky depths until he located Trojan on the riverbed and, grabbing him by his whiskers, he hauled the unconscious adult cat to the surface, dragging the limp and somewhat heavy animal to a shingle beach at the water's edge. Although he was thoroughly exhausted by his efforts Ian immediately set to work on trying to resuscitate Trojan. He blew air from his own lungs into the ginger tom's mouth and pushed down hard on his chest in an attempt to pump out any water the big cat had swallowed.

"It was an accident, I didn't mean to do it," Ian gasped between breaths. "Is that what they did to you? Now I can see why you don't like children. Come on Trojan, wake up... please don't die on me now!"

119

All of a sudden Trojan spluttered and a stream of dirty yellow river water flowed steadily from his mouth. Then he opened his one good eye and smiled. It was the first time that Ian had ever seen him smile and it came as such a welcome relief.

"Oh, I'm so glad that you're okay," cried Ian as he hugged the ginger tom. "I'm sorry Trojan, please forgive me."

Trojan raised a hefty paw and wrapped it around Ian's body as he comforted him.

"You're forgiven Kid," he growled, but in a friendly tone of voice. "Now get off me. If anyone sees me hugging you they'll think I'm going soft in my old age, and we can't have that, can we?"

"Here's your eye patch," said Ian meekly.

"Thanks Kid, but you're right; maybe I do look stupid in it. I don't think I'll ever wear it again so you can keep it as a souvenir."

"Oh no, I was only saying such an awful thing just to get at you. You look really cool in it actually, honestly you do. The eye patch is part of your character and you just wouldn't look the same without it."

Trojan accepted the eye patch and put it back on his head. By this time Spartan had arrived on the scene. It had taken him a while to catch up because the strong river current had swept them a long way downstream.

"Are you alright?" panted Spartan.

"Yeah, there's no harm done," said Trojan patting his brother on the back. "More to the point though, I've just noticed that you've found your voice again."

120

"What? Oh, I hadn't even realized with all the commotion that was going on. It must have been the shock of you falling into the river that did it. Thanks a lot Ian, you're a real hero."

Spartan grabbed hold of Ian and hugged him so tightly that he almost squeezed the last breath right out of him.

"So that's why you couldn't talk, because you were actually struck dumb? No wonder I had never heard you speak," said Ian when Spartan eventually released him from the bear-hug. "How did you lose your voice?"

"Well, I was with my brother when a firework hit him in the face and I've never been able to say a word since that day because the trauma of the ordeal affected me so much."

"I didn't know that you were brothers," said Ian in surprise.

"There's a lot of things you don't know Kid," said Trojan. "For one thing, we always knew you'd come good in the end because we had faith in you too. Anyway, that's enough idle chit-chat for now; beat it, you've got more important things to worry about, like getting some of your lives back."

Full of the joys of spring Ian was skipping merrily along the river-bank as he continued on his journey into town when a new sound reached his ears.

'BLING-BLING, ZING!' it went, and then for a second time, 'BLING-BLING, ZING!'

All of a sudden two of the black crystals on his collar reverted back to a glowing shade of amber. Ian the cat stopped momentarily to admire them and then he grinned proudly from ear to ear because he felt so pleased with himself that he had finally done something right.

CHAPTER ELEVEN

The Daylight Robberies

With a newly-found vitality in his step Ian skipped most of the way
to Coalpit Road where he discovered the back door of Pussywillow
House wide open. This was most unusual because old man Ivan
always kept it locked, so Ian proceeded with some caution as he
entered the passageway sensing that something was not quite right.
Then he heard the sound of raised voices coming from the living
room, one of which was that of Ivan whose odd accent now sounded
distinctly foreign in his currently agitated state. Whoever it was that
the old man was talking with seemed very angry and there was an
impatient note to the man's voice, but although Ian faintly
recognized it he couldn't place whom it belonged to.

Making no sound at all Ian poked his head around the living room
door in order to sneak a look at what was going on and he was quite
horrified by what he saw. Ivan was cowering in terror in his favourite
armchair whilst a thick-set man wearing a balaclava to disguise his
facial features hovered threateningly over him wielding the old

man's walking stick. It immediately became obvious to Ian that the old man was in the process of being robbed.

"Okay," said the thug, "for the last time, where's your cash? I know you have some, every old fogey has money stashed away somewhere."

"I don't have any, and even if I did I'm certainly not going to tell you where I keep it," Ivan bravely replied.

"Your tone of voice tells me you're definitely hiding something, so I'm gonna give ya one more chance old man… If ya don't tell me where your money is right now, I'll beat it out of you with your own walking stick."

In reply, Ivan simply folded his arms and stared at the robber defiantly whilst remaining tight-lipped. This seemed to annoy the intruder immensely and, raising the walking stick above his head, he took a step towards the old man but at that very moment he trod on a loose floorboard which creaked ominously underfoot and made him freeze. Ivan glanced worriedly down at the floor which caused the robber to put two and two together.

"It's under the floor isn't it?" exclaimed the robber knowingly. "You've hidden your money beneath the floorboards! I should have guessed where it was straight away 'cos all you old folk are the same – you hide your valuables in stupid places like under a mattress or a rug, or even under the floorboards. Oh, how original is that?"

Ivan stared at the robber but still he said nothing, and then he attempted to extract his aged body from his armchair and rise to his feet so that he could defend himself against the robber who was about to steal his life savings. Having briefly relaxed his arm the

124

robber raised it again and brought the walking stick crashing down on the old man's skull. Ivan slumped back into his armchair in a state of unconsciousness as a result of the heavy blow, whereupon the wicked thief cast the walking stick aside and began to busy himself with tearing up the threadbare carpet that covered the floorboards.

After helplessly watching this awful and violent incident Ian had to think fast, so without delay he shot into the kitchen and squeezed through the airbrick that led to the cavities beneath the floorboards. Crawling on his belly he scurried between the joists that supported the wooden floor until he reached the cache of money that the old man had stashed away and Ian had since moved so that he himself could steal it. However, this notion was far from his mind now because Ian was fuming at the old man's ill-treatment and the only thought in his head was to protect Ivan's life savings from falling into the hands of this wrong-doer.

The thief went at the floorboards like a madman, tearing them up one by one with a crowbar in his quest to find his spoil whilst Ian waited, patiently poised. Eventually daylight flooded into the cavity beneath the floor as the robber removed the final wooden board and located his ill-gotten earnings, and it was at this point that Ian gave the man his just reward. As the unsuspecting thief bent forwards and greedily reached for the wad of banknotes the furious tortoiseshell launched itself from between the cavity, screeching and spitting in an evil manner. With his claws at full stretch Ian anchored himself deep into the fabric of the man's balaclava and pierced the flesh of his face. Next, he began to flail mercilessly about with all four limbs.

125

Taken completely unawares the robber fell onto his back screaming in agony as he tried to remove the demented cat that was attacking him. But Ian clung on for as long as he could, gouging deep claw marks into the robber's skin so that he would easily be recognizable at a later date. Only when he assumed that enough damage had been wreaked upon the luckless raider did Ian extract his claws and leap clear. With his balaclava in tatters and nursing his wounds the would-be robber instantly scrambled to his feet and, holding his hands over his face, he fled the house empty-handed having been reduced to a gibbering wreck. After checking to ensure that Ivan was not hurt too badly Ian also fled the house satisfied that the old man was in a comfortable condition.

'BLING-BLING, ZING!'

Another crystal on Ian's collar rekindled itself but he was too busy to notice because he was on an important mission.

As fast as his legs would move Ian raced along the streets until he reached Number 10 Catkin Mews where he vaulted over the garden fence, clearing it in one fell swoop. Luckily for him there was a soft landing awaiting his arrival. Slightly dazed by his rude awakening Adolf the dog got to his feet and shook his body violently.

"YOU!" he exclaimed in surprise. "I thought I told you never to set foot in my garden ever again. Now I'm going to have to teach you not to trespass."

"Hold it!" Ian interrupted. "I haven't got time for this… I'm sorry for upsetting you the last time I came here, but now I am on an errand of mercy because I urgently need your help."

"Why should I help you?"

126

"It's not really me who needs your help – it's a friend of mine actually."

With a puzzled expression on his face Adolf cocked his head on one side and listened closely as Ian related the story of the events that had taken place in Ivan's home. Eventually the dog's puzzled look changed to one of concern.

"Then there's no time to lose... We need to act fast," said Adolf.

"Oh, thank-you so much Adolf, I will be forever in your debt. You see, I am just a cat that people don't take much notice of but you are a large dog who has the capability of barking loudly, therefore you can raise the alarm when you bark and human help will quickly arrive on the scene."

"Indeed," Adolf agreed. "Leave it to me; I know exactly what needs to be done."

"There is nothing else I can do to help Ivan, so while you're taking care of him there is another thing that I have to put right... See you later," said Ian and he set off in the direction of the affluent side of town.

'BLING-BLING, ZING!'

Once again, an amber crystal began to shine on Ian's collar for he had just carried out yet another good deed.

When Ian arrived at his next destination he squashed his nose against a pane of glass in the conservatory so that he could have a good look inside. At first he couldn't see Phillip but when he spotted him the tortoiseshell cat was quite astounded because, curled up in a flowery-patterned cat basket edged with fancy lace trim, he saw an

127

overweight ball of fur. Poor Phillip had put on so much weight that it was hard to recognize him from the athletic animal he was when Ian had first met him back in the Limbo Room at Catland. When Ian tapped hard on the glass pane the pampered house-cat turned a podgy face towards him and opened its bulging eyes.

"Go away and leave me to sleep," scowled Phillip.

"Man, you need to get some exercise," was all Ian could manage to say to the forlorn looking Persian.

"Yeah? Well, if you'd gone to see The Catmaster when I asked you I wouldn't be so fat now would I? All this good living has gone straight to my belly. It's not easy to say 'no' when they're offering you platefuls of oily fish washed down with saucers of yummy double cream, you know."

Ian lowered his head shamefully.

"I'm sorry Phillip, I really am," he said apologetically.

"It's Lulabelle actually!"

"Okay, if that's what you want to be called: I'm sorry Lulabelle. I was a selfish cat when I saw you last and all I was thinking about were my own needs, but I'm a changed person now and I've come to rescue you."

"I don't want to be rescued, I like it here and I've got used to living this new lifestyle. It's a different world to me and something that I've never experienced before... you know, being a gypsy cat and all that. You don't realize how difficult it is to survive out there. It's like this you see: my owners feed me all the time so I no longer have to hunt for my dinner, I don't have to be outside in all weathers

128

any more, and I'm treated like a king. What more could a cat ask for? No Sirree, this is the life for me... I feel great."

"But you look terrible and your present lifestyle can't be at all good for you," Ian tried to convince the fat cat.

"I've already told you that I feel great, so mind your own business, will you? Now, if you don't mind, I have an appointment with my pet shampooer later today (my roots are beginning to show through and I can't do a thing with my fur) so I need to get some beauty sleep in before she gets here. Goodbye."

"Aw, come on Phillip..."

"LULABELLE!"

"Whatever! Look, you've got to come with me. I came to get you out of here and I'm not leaving empty-handed."

"Goodbye," Phillip repeated before rolling over and turning his back on Ian.

The frustrated tortoiseshell tapped frantically on the glass as he tried to get Phillip's attention again but the contented house-cat deliberately ignored him. In the end Ian had no choice but to give up and walk away. However, he was not admitting defeat so easily because he knew that he had to save the confused animal, and not just from his over-powering owners either. No, he had to save Phillip from himself also because his new lifestyle seemed to have gone to his head as well as his belly.

A short while later the pet shampooer arrived at the posh house and this was the very moment Ian had been waiting for so that he could get inside the building. The front door had been left wide open so that the shampooer could carry her equipment indoors and Ian seized this opportunity to sneak in. Once he was safely inside the clever tortoiseshell located the fire alarm system and set it off. Immediately, the home owners, the shampooer and two other house guests evacuated the premises. Meanwhile, as all the furore was taking place, Ian made his way through the beautifully decorated interior of the posh house until he reached the conservatory where he found the petrified Persian who was too afraid to go outside and too fat to escape.

"What are you doing here?" asked Phillip in a woeful tone of voice. "Was it you who set the house on fire?"

"It's not on fire, it's a false alarm. I know it's not right to do things like that but I told you that I'd rescue you and it was the only plan I could come up with."

"And I've told you that I didn't want to leave. Now get out of here or I'll scream the house down, and when my owners catch you they will have you put in a cats' home."

"Nobody will hear you with the sound of the alarms going off. Besides, they all followed the fire drill procedure correctly and now they're waiting at the foot of the garden for the Fire Brigade to arrive."

Suddenly Phillip began to cry and shriek at the top of his voice.

"Wah!" he sobbed. "I want my mummy, I want my daddy, I want my nice dinner.... Wah!"

"Oh, for goodness sake pull yourself together and snap out of it," yelled Ian, but Phillip carried on wailing.

Ian glanced at Phillip's dinner bowl and thought about giving it to him just to keep the spoilt baby quiet, but then another idea came into his head. He dug his claws into the dinner bowl and pulled out a piece of wet, oily fish which he held firmly by the tail before slapping Phillip firmly across the face with it, not once but twice.

SLAP! SLOP!

In complete astonishment Phillip froze on the spot, an expression of complete horror taking over his chubby features. Then he shook his head from side to side and began to purse his lips.

"Ooh", he said in a completely different voice. "I feel so much better already – I don't know what had come over me lately."

It appeared that the slaps Phillip had received across his face had done the trick and now he was back to his normal self.

"The reason you have ended up like you are is because you have been suffering from delusions of grandeur," Ian explained, "together with a bad case of over-indulgence and lack of fresh air. Now come along, let's get out of here."

"But I'm too fat, I can't even walk any more," Phillip complained.

"Then I shall have to carry you across my shoulders. I don't care what I have to do, let's just go before it's too late."

Ian hoisted his friend onto his shoulders and with his limbs almost buckling under the other cat's weight they fled the posh house escaping with only seconds to spare because a fire tender had already turned up and it would not be long before the crew discovered that it had been a false alarm.

"Oh, it feels so good to be free again, all thanks to you Ian," said Phillip once the two escapees were outside in the garden.

"You don't have to thank me," panted Ian. "It's my fault you were in this mess in the first place 'cos I mixed up the spells in Catland."

"Oh, you did, did you?" Phillip said quite angrily but then he paused to think about things for a moment or two before adding: "Never mind, it doesn't really matter because everything has worked out well in the end. I shan't hold a grudge against you for any of this, so don't worry."

Very soon the two cats had left the garden of the large house far behind them and were safely out in the street. Exhausted by his efforts Ian collapsed in a heap on the ground and Phillip gently rolled off his shoulders.

"That's a huge weight off, isn't it?" laughed Phillip.

"You're not kidding!" Ian agreed.

Suddenly, another voice came out of nowhere, scaring both Ian and Phillip half to death and abruptly ending their conversation.

"We'll take him from here," was the familiar growl.

Ian looked up in surprise and saw Trojan and Spartan towering over his worn-out body. He noticed that Trojan was sporting his eye patch with pride once again and Ian felt extremely pleased about this.

"Well done Kid, we knew you'd be able to find a way of getting him out," growled Trojan.

"Yep, you stole poor old Phillip away from the lap of luxury and now we're here to take him back to reality," chuckled Spartan.

Phillip put his paws over his eyes and began to groan at the thought of this.

Winking at the youngster, Spartan patted Ian fondly on the head and then the two ginger toms departed without saying another word, effortlessly carrying their hefty burden between them. As he watched his trio of friends depart a pleasantly rewarding sound rang in Ian's ears.

'BLING-BLING, ZING!'

A fifth amber crystal had come back to life on Ian's collar and the tortoiseshell cat smiled contentedly, yet briefly, because his thoughts quickly turned to the welfare of the old man Ivan.

CHAPTER TWELVE

Back to Court

Pussywillow House was now in darkness. Having returned during the late afternoon Ian had found Ivan's abode to be deserted with all doors and windows tightly secured. All he could do now was wait to hear some news regarding the old man's health and hope that Ivan was going to fully recover. It was a cold, crisp December evening and Ian accepted that he may have a long wait ahead of him so he went to the coal bunker and located the sheepskin rug that Sorcha had stored away for his benefit. Using his teeth he tugged out the rug and settled down for his vigil, grateful that Sorcha had rescued the rug after he had thrown it into the river. Fortunately Ian did not have to wait long for something to happen because at six o'clock that evening he was disturbed by an uncanny meowing sound that reached his ears in stereo.

"Harlequin The Catmaster requires the pleasure of your company," chanted the two Siamese cats in their sing-song fashion.

Ian drew a long breath and sighed deeply.

"Typical!" he murmured out loud. "Just when I thought things were improving for me, everything suddenly goes horribly wrong. Now that's put me in a bit of a dilemma."

Then he sighed again, as if the weight of the world lay upon his furry shoulders.

"I'm sorry to have to turn down The Catmaster's request but I really can't come with you because I'm waiting for news of Ivan," he told the Siamese cats.

"Harlequin asked us to inform you that he – the old man that is – will be fine and there is nothing further to worry about," said the Siamese reassuringly.

"The old man is going to be fine you say? But how does he know that for sure?"

"Trust us… He knows!" was the stereophonic answer.

"Well, if that's the case, then I shall be only too happy to accept his request to see me," replied a relieved Ian.

"We are very pleased to hear that," echoed the Siamese cats. "Be at Catland within the hour."

Then they turned to leave.

"Wait!" Ian shouted after them.

The Siamese cats hesitated and exchanged glances before turning around again to face Ian.

"I apologize for the way that I treated you when we first met," he said. "It was very wrong of me to fight with you and I've learned to adopt a new attitude since then."

With a grin on their faces the Siamese sisters willingly accepted

Ian's apology by nodding their heads gracefully in unison. When they had finished their routine they continued on their way.

Immediately following their departure the tortoiseshell cat hastily bundled up his sheepskin rug and shoved it back into the coal bunker before setting off on his journey to Catland. Once he had left his home town behind a hazy blue light suddenly lit the trail ahead of him and the beautiful apparition of his guardian angel cat known as Sorcha suddenly materialized in its midst.

"I told you to have faith Ian, and you did. I'm so proud of you," she said in her velvety, softly-purring voice.

"Thank-you Sorcha, but if it wasn't for your guidance things may well have been different."

"There's no need to thank me Ian because you really did it alone. Only you could have followed your heart and chosen the right path. It would be an honour for me to accompany you to Catland for the last time, would you mind if I did?"

"Of course I don't mind, I shall be more than happy to walk with you by my side… Did you say 'for the last time?' "

"That was a slip of the tongue again; it's getting to be a common mistake I keep making."

"What's going to happen to me when I get to Catland?" asked Ian with a worried look on his face.

"Wait and see. But don't worry about a thing because I think you're going to be pleased about this particular visit."

Together, the happy duo strolled along the river bank until they arrived at the foot of Sunrise Hill where several dozen red squirrels had lined up on either side of the front entrance to Catland holding miniscule flaming torches of fire aloft in their tiny paws, their silky red fur glowing a shade of orange in the dancing light. Gubbins was also there to greet them, his bony frame and facial features appearing more alien-like than ever as he stood outlined by the flickering firelight at the centre of the entrance.

"It gives me great pleasure to welcome you on this fine evening Ian, as our newest member of Catland," announced the ecstatic Devon Rex. "Please follow me."

Ian was flabbergasted by this statement.

"Can I use the front door now that I'm a member?" he asked.

"Yes, you can use the front door now," replied Gubbins with a grin on his face. "Come along."

Led by their queen Sciurus fifty red squirrels then marched into the maze of dark catacombs which burst into light as the torch-bearers entered, followed by Gubbins, with Ian and Sorcha walking side by side close behind him. The bulk of the red squirrel army brought up the rear and the huge stone in the hillside that concealed the entrance to Catland closed shut behind them forever. The strange procession traipsed through the underground labyrinth, all the while climbing uphill until they finally arrived at the vast chamber that was the court of The Catmaster.

When they got there the courtroom was already packed full of cats, just as it had been on Ian's first visit to Catland; however, the atmosphere felt decidedly different tonight. It seemed that every single cat that existed throughout the World had come to see Ian for this very occasion. As was customary, Trojan and Spartan escorted the tortoiseshell cat across the courtroom to the now familiar stone pulpit where a comfy, cushioned chair had recently been introduced. After making sure that Ian was quite comfortable the two ginger sentries took their places on either side of Harlequin's throne whereupon two Siamese cats immediately appeared and flanked each of them. Gubbins was already seated at his end of the table whilst Sorcha was the last cat to take her position and she took a seat at the opposite end of the table to Gubbins. A burble of excited chatter filled the electrifying air within the courtroom which ceased at the very moment that Gubbins jumped to his feet and commanded the words:

"ALL RISE!"

Every member of the cat congregation rose to their feet to respectfully observe in silence as the crimson-robed figure of Harlequin The Catmaster entered the courtroom and positioned himself upon his throne.

"Please be seated," was Gubbins' next command.

At this request the entire throng sat down, all except for Ian who had remembered that he wasn't allowed to sit down during his previous trial.

"You may be seated also," Gubbins told him. "That's why we have furnished a chair for you."

"I know there's a first time for everything, but I was being polite," said Ian. Nevertheless, he willingly sat down because his legs had turned to jelly as he tried to anticipate what was going to happen to him.

There was a murmur of laughter that spread throughout the

audience upon hearing this remark but silence quickly resumed as Harlequin began to speak.

"The time period for the Sentence of Nine Lives is tonight drawing to a close," he uttered. "The hour has come to conclude this momentous event and show our findings. Before the final judgement is passed do you have anything to say Ian?"

Ian cleared his throat nervously.

"Do you mind if I stand up?" he asked.

"Whatever makes you feel comfortable," said The Catmaster. "You can stand on your head if you wish, or turn cartwheels across the floor – after all, the stage is currently all yours to prove yourself of worth."

From that moment on all of the cats' eyes and ears in the courtroom were fixed upon him as the tortoiseshell slowly got to his feet and began his defence.

"In the past I know that I've been a really bad boy (and a bad cat for that matter) but I am trying to make things right. I would just like to say that I am truly sorry for being so mean to my parents, to my sister, to Adolf the dog, to Phillip, Sorcha, Harlequin and any other cats I have upset along the way. I am learning to change my ways and it feels so much better to be in people's good books. So, please, please, PLEASE can I change back into a boy again? You really have taught me a valuable lesson about life."

An eerie hush followed Ian's statement before Harlequin broke the silent atmosphere when he began to whisper amongst the guests who were assembled at his table, and then he put on his half-moon spectacles and spoke up so that every cat and squirrel could hear.

"Well, young man, as I read through these notes I have upon my table it appears that you didn't regain all of the eight lives that you lost. In fact, you only recovered five of them."

Ian's jaw dropped when he heard this news and his eyes began to cloud over.

"However," Harlequin went on, "we are in agreement that you are trying exceptionally hard to become a better person and having made your apologies to everyone concerned that alone will be sufficient to warrant you merit. I promised you that if you had lives left intact at the end of your time period then a human boy you would once again become and, as a man... er, I mean a cat... of my word I shall keep that promise."

Harlequin waved his paws in the air and all nine crystals on Ian's collar lit up to radiate a bright amber glow that surrounded his head like a halo. Ian admired his collar with pure delight, beaming broadly from ear to ear, but then the smile quickly disappeared when he realized he had not changed back into a human being.

"But I'm still a cat," he said despondently.

"That's because you are still in Catland. You will be restored to a boy shortly, upon your return to the mortal world."

A relieved smile instantly spread across Ian's face.

"Before I go back to my mortal world, can I ask a couple of questions?" he enquired.

"Of course you may."

"Firstly, I've noticed that Phillip is not here to see me off and that's such a shame because I like Phillip... Where is he?"

"Poor old Phillip is in the process of being transformed back into the slim, black, long-haired style of cat that he used to be before obesity got the better of him. He is actually visiting a health farm at the present moment, trying to lose some weight. I have no doubt that he will be fit again soon enough to venture back into the outside world."

"I'm glad to hear such good news," said Ian. "I was quite worried about him for a while."

This was followed by another hesitant pause from Ian that lasted until Harlequin eventually piped up to break the hush.

"And your next question is?" he asked, trying to spur Ian on.

"Yes, my second question is this: if I had lost all nine lives would you really have turned me into a Permanent Cat?"

Harlequin looked at Gubbins and the pair of wizard cats began to snigger.

"No!" they said in harmony between giggles.

And then the whole audience began to laugh.

"What's so funny?" shouted Ian trying to make himself heard above the din. But he couldn't get an answer until the laughter had died away.

"Well..." said Gubbins at length. "The truth of the matter is that we didn't really have the power to carry out our threat – and that's all it was, a threat."

"I don't understand," said Ian.

"The spell was only temporary. We simply wanted to frighten you so that you would change your ways... And, by jingo, it worked!"

"So the whole thing was a set-up?"

"Everything," explained Gubbins.

"Even my aggressive attitude towards you," Trojan interrupted. "I was merely demonstrating what it was like to be you."

"Then you're not blind either?"

"Oh yes, unfortunately I most certainly am."

"What of the robbery at Pussywillow House, was that staged too?" asked Ian turning towards Harlequin for an answer.

"Yes, that was also a put-up job. Mind you, we weren't expecting you to jump on the robber's face and try to rip him to shreds. That reaction of yours was a complete surprise to us and a little unfortunate for our friend Jim," Harlequin told him.

"And what about you Sorcha? Are you really a Permanent Cat?"

"Yes, I am Ian... However, I think you are still misunderstanding us though. We are all very real and everything about us is real too; it was purely the plot that was made up in order to force you into situations that would cause you to react and change your outlook on life."

"Oh, now I see. How clever of you all. Then I really have to thank everyone for saving me from my own self-destruction."

"I would like to say that it was a pleasure but in reality it was darned hard work," laughed Harlequin. "Regardless of that, we got the desired result and that's all that matters in the end. Now, time is marching swiftly on so I think we should release you... Gubbins, would you do the business please?"

"It'll be a pleasure M'Lord," said Gubbins as he waved his bony limbs wildly about him. In that instant the collar around Ian's neck vanished into thin air.

"Very good me old son, you're getting better at this wizardry lark all the time," Harlequin said with a proud smile upon his face as he praised his assistant.

Ian placed his paws around his neck noting how odd it seemed now that the collar had gone, although he felt as if he had gained his freedom back again. At the same time he thought hard about Harlequin's last comment, knowing that he had heard that expression somewhere before.

"Gubbins is your son?" exclaimed the bewildered tortoiseshell.

"No, I'm his assistant, I just help him out," Gubbins hurriedly answered.

"Moving swiftly on..." Harlequin interrupted loudly. "Please queue here ladies and gentlemen to say a fond farewell to our reformed friend Ian."

The whole audience promptly flocked around the tortoiseshell cat to embrace him and shake his hand before his departure. This was followed by another procession from the courtroom to the passageway that Ian had originally travelled along when he had climbed the great white oak tree on top of Sunrise Hill. Once they had escorted Ian to this point the crowd turned around and went back into the courtroom leaving the tortoiseshell cat alone in the tunnel with The Catmaster.

"I thought I was allowed to use the front door now that I'm a member of Catland," said Ian in a slightly disappointed tone of voice.

"All doors are the same now Ian. You will find that each one leads in the right direction," explained Harlequin. "You have chosen

143

the true path to your destiny... Good-bye for now and best wishes for the future."

Harlequin The Catmaster held out a large furry paw and shook firmly with the youngster.

"By the way, it is precisely two minutes to midnight on Christmas Eve and I promised that you would be home for Christmas... Merry Christmas Ian!"

Having had the final word Harlequin smiled warmly before returning to the courtroom through the arched doorway. Ian heard the lock fall into place as the door slammed shut and he was alone in the dark earthen tunnel. All of a sudden there was a blinding flash of light as if a lightning bolt had struck, and then there was darkness.

CHAPTER THIRTEEN

Catland Revisited

The boy opened his eyes wide, gazing blankly at his bedroom ceiling as he tried to focus. Meanwhile, a look of woe upon his sister's face immediately turned to joy and tears streamed down her ashen cheeks. She had been on the midnight watch at his bedside.

"Mum! Mum!" she shrieked. "Ian's awake… He's awake!"

Mum came thundering across the landing and was in the bedroom within a split-second of receiving this news.

"Quick Ellie, fetch your father," urged Mum.

But Dad couldn't have failed to hear the commotion and he was already at his son's bedside.

The boy then rolled his eyes, looked at his family and a huge smile cracked his face in two.

"I'm back!" he muttered excitedly, and then to his family he said: "What's all the fuss about?"

"Oh, Ian, we've been so worried about you. This is the best Christmas present we could ever have wished for," said Mum.

"Yes, Merry Christmas Son," agreed his father in a shaky voice as he choked back the tears.

"Merry Christmas Ian," echoed the boy's sister.

"It was all a dream. I've just had the most bizarre dream!" exclaimed Ian, partly to himself. "…And you all called me Ian when I thought my name was Thomas."

"It is, but we've always called you Ian ever since you were a nipper," his mother replied. "I don't know where it came from but it's a name you asked us to call you because you preferred it to Thomas. Do you remember?"

"Oh yes, I remember now – how weird! But everything else was all a dream, right?"

"No Ian, it wasn't a dream. You've been in a coma for several weeks, ever since the incident on Sunrise Hill," Ian's mother told him.

"Incident? What incident?"

"Nobody knows what really happened but a travelling man – you know, a gypsy fellow – found you unconscious beside a burnt-out tree stump that's been there for years apparently."

Ian sat bolt upright in his bed.

"You mean the great white oak has been burned down?" he shrieked in panic.

"You seem surprised, Son. The tree was struck by lightning years ago," Ian's father explained. "It happened long before I moved to this area when I was a small boy. It's always been a burnt-out hollow tree stump ever since I can remember."

"I don't believe you! I must go and take a look for myself," cried Ian pulling back his quilt and trying to get out of bed.

"No, you haven't been well. Rest is what you need right now my boy," Ian's father assured him.

"But Dad, I feel fine. I'm as right as rain, honestly I am."

"No! You're going nowhere and that's final."

Ian's father was adamant. He pulled the quilt back over his son once again and tucked him in, so Ian had no choice but to stay put.

"When did you come home?" Ian asked his father.

"I returned on the day after your mishap. I decided that running away from home wasn't the answer to my problems so I came back to face matters and then you had your accident."

Ian smiled at his father.

"I'm so glad you're home," he said. "I'm sorry for all the problems that I've caused and from now on things will be different, just you wait and see. And I'm sorry to you too Ellie for all the unkind things I've ever said to you."

"That's okay," said Ellie in a soft whisper.

"I shall never bully you again Sis... I love you."

"I love you too," said Ellie and she began to cry again.

"Are we still broke Mum?" asked Ian.

"Well, no, not really," replied his mother. "Good fortune has smiled down upon us and we've had a bit of a windfall. Strangely enough, an old man came by just this afternoon and handed me a package. He told me that he knew you and the package was a gift to help with our family's recovery. After the gentleman had gone I opened the package and found several thousand pounds wrapped up inside."

"Do you know who the man is, Mum?" asked Ian.

"I have never set eyes on him before. He was a complete stranger to me. I've no idea who he was and if I had known what he was giving us I wouldn't have accepted it. We might not have much, but I do have a certain amount of pride you know."

"Yes I know, and I think that I also know who the stranger is," admitted Ian.

"Then you must give the money back to that person as soon as possible," said Mum. "In the meantime, it's late and we should really get some sleep. Tomorrow – well, today actually because it's long past midnight – is going to be a huge celebration, not just for Christmas but also because you've come back to us. That's a miracle in itself."

Having hugged and kissed Ian until he was blue in the face, his parents and sister returned to their bedrooms for the best night's sleep they were to have had in a long time. However, Ian did not feel in the least bit tired and as soon as dawn broke he picked up the package and quietly sneaked out of the house.

Running like the wind Ian sped along the river bank, not once glancing upwards because he was looking out for obstacles on the ground that he might trip over. It was only when he arrived at the foot of Sunrise Hill did he raise his head. When he looked up he saw a grey mass of swirling cloud, full of snow, hanging over the hilltop like a veil and it was not possible to see the summit let alone the great white oak tree. After Ian had clambered to the peak his face fell in dismay for there, just as his father had told him, was a blackened hollow tree stump. Sunrise Hill and the great white oak tree were nothing like Ian had remembered them to be.

For an unknown amount of time the boy stared at the solitary black stump, numb to the bone from both the affect of his discovery and also from the biting wind that whistled all around him. After a short while it began to snow, slowly at first, but it quickly developed into a blizzard. And then out of the blizzard came a huddled figure dressed in black.

The stranger appeared to be a travelling man – possibly a gypsy – and he was unusually plump too for someone who lived off the land. Although his features were mostly covered with a hooded garment Ian noticed that the man's eyes were as black as coal, not unlike his father's eyes, and so too was the colour of his unkempt hair where it had popped into view. The dark stranger stood beside the boy and neither of them spoke because they were purely gazing at the blackened monument that was now the remnant of the great white oak. Following another unaccountable length of time the stranger turned his head towards Ian and whispered three words.

"Merry Christmas Ian."

That was all he said and then he began to walk away.

"How do you know my name?" asked the boy.

But the stranger kept on walking.

"Who are you?" Ian shouted after him.

"You know who I am," said the parting traveller.

"No I don't... Please tell me your name."

"Phillip," was the reply and then the stranger vanished into the swirling mist that surrounded Sunrise Hill.

By the time Ian reached Coalpit Road the blizzard had subsided, giving way to only light snow flurries, and several inches of virgin snow lay twinkling upon the ground as if the winter fairies had sprinkled it with glitter. Bedecked with fairy lights and other seasonal decorations Pussywillow House appeared different now with its warm, welcoming glow. Not only that, but it seemed that it had been given a facelift because the cottage had been fitted with new windows and doors, and it was freshly-decorated too.

Still clutching the package full of money in his hand Ian drew a sharp intake of breath before rapping on the front door with its shiny new knocker made from brass and shaped like an Egyptian sphinx. In no time at all, showing no sign of his previous frailty, old man Ivan opened the front door and invited the boy inside.

"Welcome Ian," he said gleefully, "we've been expecting you. Please come in and make yourself at home. You should know where everything is by now although there have been a few minor changes around here."

Ian was speechless but, nonetheless, he did as he was asked. Once inside, he observed that the interior of the cottage appeared different too, suddenly benefiting from a complete makeover. Even the airbrick in the kitchen had been filled in and there was no sign of it ever having existed. The youngster held out his hand, attempting to pass the package to Ivan, but the old man declined the offer.

"It's a gift," he said, "for your family. I know that they work hard and they still struggle, regardless of what your mum tells you, so maybe some extra cash will help out. I spent a little money doing up this place and found that there was some left over so I thought of your mother. Go on, take it – she deserves it."

"Okay, if you insist, but…"

"But nothing, it's yours. I'm sure you will find a way of getting her to accept my gift. Now don't let me hear another word on the subject. Please come with me and meet my dinner guests."

When Ian arrived in the living room there were five people waiting to greet him, all of whom seemed strangely familiar as if Ian had already met them. Ivan first introduced the young boy to two burly gentlemen with flame-red hair.

"These are my friends from Scotland, Tartan and Sporran. Well, that's what I call them anyway. Tartan is blind and his brother has to guide him wherever he goes."

"How ya doing Kid?" Tartan greeted him.

Sporran cheekily winked an eye at Ian but he said nothing.

"And these two ladies are their wives Tia and Mia. They're twins who come from the Orient you know – such lovely people."

Ian stared in disbelief at the two Eastern beauties who were elegantly sipping tea from dainty china cups. The twins smiled sweetly at Ian and nodded their heads slowly in a gesture of acknowledgment.

"We are pleased to meet you Ian," they chimed in a sort of sing-song harmony.

"And lastly, but by no means least, this is my good friend Rex Buggins. I've known him for years – we first met when I was on holiday in the county of Devon… He's my home help, you know."

A skinny little fellow with big ears and bulging eyes immediately leapt up from the sofa and launched himself towards Ian, throwing his arms high in the air and waving them wildly around like a windmill. This made Ian almost jump out of his skin.

"Hi!" said Rex Buggins. "Sorry, but I didn't mean to startle you. I always like to greet people that way."

Having made himself known the strange-looking man spun rapidly around and threw his body down onto the sofa again, beaming like a lunatic.

"One of our guests hasn't arrived yet but that's expected because he's always late," laughed Ivan. "Sometimes he doesn't even turn up at all because he is forever becoming lost or getting sent to the wrong place! He's a bit of a nomadic fellow really who goes by the name of Phillip."

"I… I saw him a short while ago on top of Sunrise Hill," Ian informed him.

"Oh, then he'll probably be along soon. Or maybe he won't. Only time will tell."

Deep in his sub-conscious mind Ian had been aware that the guests in Ivan's home were very familiar but it wasn't until now that he was positive he did already know them. The only cat who was missing from the picture at this present moment was Sorcha. Ian wondered what had become of his beautiful guardian angel, the Permanent Cat.

"Is your name really Ivan?" asked Ian.

"Yes, it really is Ivan – Ivan Goluboy to be exact. Goluboy should be spelt with a 'j' instead of a 'y' but I spell it how it sounds, it's easier for people to pronounce. It's an old Russian word meaning 'Blue'."

At that moment Ian's eyes wandered towards the new patio windows at the far end of the living room. Beyond the glass structure he had suddenly noticed a large tree at the bottom of the garden and that is what had drawn his attention.

IT WAS THE GREAT WHITE OAK!

Ian was overjoyed to see that the tree was still in existence albeit in an entirely different location. The magnificent specimen soared high into the grey, snowy skies, its ghostly outstretched limbs – formerly a shade of white when seen in a certain light – now giving off a warm amber hue. And it was alive too! Its huge branches were teeming with red squirrels and even from such a distance he could tell that all of their beady little eyes were focused upon him.

Now there was no doubt in his mind at all. He was positive that he had previously been acquainted with everyone at Pussywillow House and he became aware at that precise moment that Catland wasn't so much an imaginary secret world as it was a place where people and animals could live in harmony together. And he also believed that animals could teach the human race so much about rights and wrongs because they were pure and innocent. At that same moment he came to understand that Sunrise Hill was not strictly the Earthgate to Catland after all because it was merely a stepping stone, and the real Earthgate was wherever the tree went in its quest to seek righteousness.

"I have to go home now," announced Ian, snapping out of his dreamlike trance. "My family will be wondering where I am. It's Christmas morning and I need to spend some time with them."

"I understand," said Ivan, placing his arm around the boy's shoulders. "You do realize that you can visit us any time you want, don't you?"

Ian nodded his head.

"Now that you have been tamed you are one of us now Ian because you are a fully fledged member of the breed *Felis Cattus Domesticus*.

"What does that mean?" asked Ian.

"Ask your father, he will be able to explain," replied Ivan. "Always bear in mind though, that although you now possess the gift of having extra senses you don't really have nine lives, so be careful out there. Oh, there is one more thing before you leave… We have a present to give you."

Ivan threw open the patio doors and a beautiful chocolate and cream coloured Birman cat immediately rushed into the house.

"SORCHA!" cried the boy in pure delight.

"She's a gift from all of us and she's all yours. Take her home with you and always love and cherish her," Ivan told him.

"Oh I will," said Ian, picking up his dear little friend and hugging her close to his heart. "I promise that I'll take great care of her."

"Yes, I'm sure you will," agreed Ivan. "Good-bye for now Ian, see you soon."

154

"Good-bye Ivan and thank-you for everything... Good-bye everyone."

"MERRY CHRISTMAS IAN", chorused all the guests as Ian departed from Pussywillow House. "See you again very soon."

The first thing Ian did when he stepped outside was to go directly to the coal bunker in Ivan's garden and take out the sheepskin rug. Then he wrapped it around Sorcha.

"There, that should keep you warm", he said. "You've been out in the cold for far too long Sorcha and never again will you find yourself all alone."

The pretty cat gazed lovingly at Ian and purred happily as she snuggled cosily into the warmth of the blanket.

As he walked along Coalpit Road cradling his Permanent Cat tightly in his arms Ian saw Jim the milkman driving towards the old man's cottage on his regular morning round. He noticed also that the poor man's face was covered with deep scratches that resembled claw marks.

"Whoops!" said Ian burying his face deep into the sheepskin rug so that Jim didn't see him.

"Meeow! Yeeow! Ow!" said Sorcha, and she winked knowingly at him.

THE END

Look out for these other amazing titles from Wolfren Riverstick, coming soon

The Incredible Adventures of Amanda and Skelly

When Amanda James moves from her home in the city to live in the countryside she feels extremely lonely at first. However, she soon befriends a creature known as 'Skelly' who has been stranded on Earth since crashing his space egg after accidentally departing from his home planet of Laktose in the distant galaxy of the Milky Way. This is just the beginning of a series of remarkable adventures between these two new friends.

Amanda Goes To Laktose
(Introducing Boggles The Lab Rat)

In the second book of the 'Amanda and Skelly' series our young heroine sets off in search of her missing friend, ultimately paying a visit to the planet of Laktose, whereupon more hilarious romps develop.

While You Sleep...

Have you ever wondered where your dreams and nightmares come from? Well, wonder no longer because all is revealed in this fascinating insight into the unknown world of sleep. Meet The Dremlocks, The Inkybyes, the Jackson family... and find out what you would never have guessed about hamsters.